NATURE'S
WAY

Publishers of the International Library

LIBRAIRIE ERNEST FLAMMARION—France

VERLAG J. F. SCHREIBER—Germany
(in association with Union Verlag, Stuttgart, and Oster. Bundesverlag, Vienna)

COLLINS PUBLISHERS—Great Britain

RIZZOLI EDITORE—Italy

McGRAW-HILL BOOK COMPANY—United States of America

DAVID STEPHEN and JAMES LOCKIE

NATURE'S WAY

A look at the web of life

COLLINS London and Glasgow

First edition 1969

Printed in Italy
Rizzoli Editore—Milan

CONTENTS

INTRODUCTION

Ecology is the study of life—not just strands in the web of life, but the whole web. It is a way of looking at life, and a method of discovering facts. It is the study of animals and plants, their relationships to each other, and to their total environment.

Man is a strand in the web of life, related in some way to every other strand, and unable to exist independently of sunshine, soil, water, minerals, plants or other animals. He is part of nature; not an onlooker.

As a science, ecology is a kind of No Man's Land around other sciences. It gives to the others, and takes from them; it illuminates them and is illuminated by them. It is a way of looking at them all—zoology, botany, geology, climatology, biology and the pursuits of agriculture, forestry, medicine and wildlife management.

Ecology is also an adventure—in a field so vast that no one has yet trodden on more than a fraction of it. Only when the field has been completely explored will man achieve working harmony with his environment.

Leveret of the European Brown Hare on rough pasture in spring.

CHAPTER I

THE LIVING SOIL

Soil is the ground we walk on—the land mass of the earth—the landscape before our eyes. Soil is rock; but rock does not become soil until it has been worked upon by nature's alchemy. Rock is the parent, and soil, like any offspring, bears its parent's likeness. The soil's structure and basic nature are inherited from the parent rock; they can be added to, and taken away from, but they cannot be destroyed.

All soils have this simple beginning. Frost, wind, ice and rain work on the rock surface—grinding, breaking down, refining. Simple plants like mosses and lichens add their acids to the rubble. Climate and living organisms, plant and animal—from the microscopic and minute to the very large—add heart and life to make it into the life-giving medium we know as soil. But rock does not become soil in a year, or a century. The top is not worn off a boulder in a man's lifetime.

Once lichens have gained a foothold on the weathered rubble they begin to break it down still further. Dust and rock particles gather on the lichens, and when the lichens die new minerals and organic matter are added to the forming soil. Mosses take hold, then ferns with their luxuriant growth. These add further organic matter when they die down. Bacteria, fungi, and microscopic animals invade the young soil—living, dying and multiplying—enriching and deepening it with their waste products and dead bodies. Soon it can support pioneering annual grasses and herbs, then the perennial types, and eventually trees and shrubs.

There are as many soil types as there are parent bedrocks. Alkaline soils come from limestone; acid ones come from sandstone. Granite and quartzite produce gritty or gravelly soils. The clays come from feldspar. But soils have not all remained permanently on their parent bed; nor do they now. So the soil blanket is not always a safe guide to the identity of the bed underneath.

Soil on the move

Soil, and the makings of soil, can be moved. They have been moved and are still being moved, for the forces of nature are never idle.

Thousands of years ago the glaciers of the last Ice Age bulldozed whole landscapes of rock and rubble and dust and carried them far from their source. Mountains of soil were tipped into the sea, or left behind as terminal moraines of mud where the melting glaciers began their retreat. The mud dried and was blown far away by the wind, to be trapped against hill barriers

The glaciers are nature's bulldozers, able to move mountains of soil and rubble.

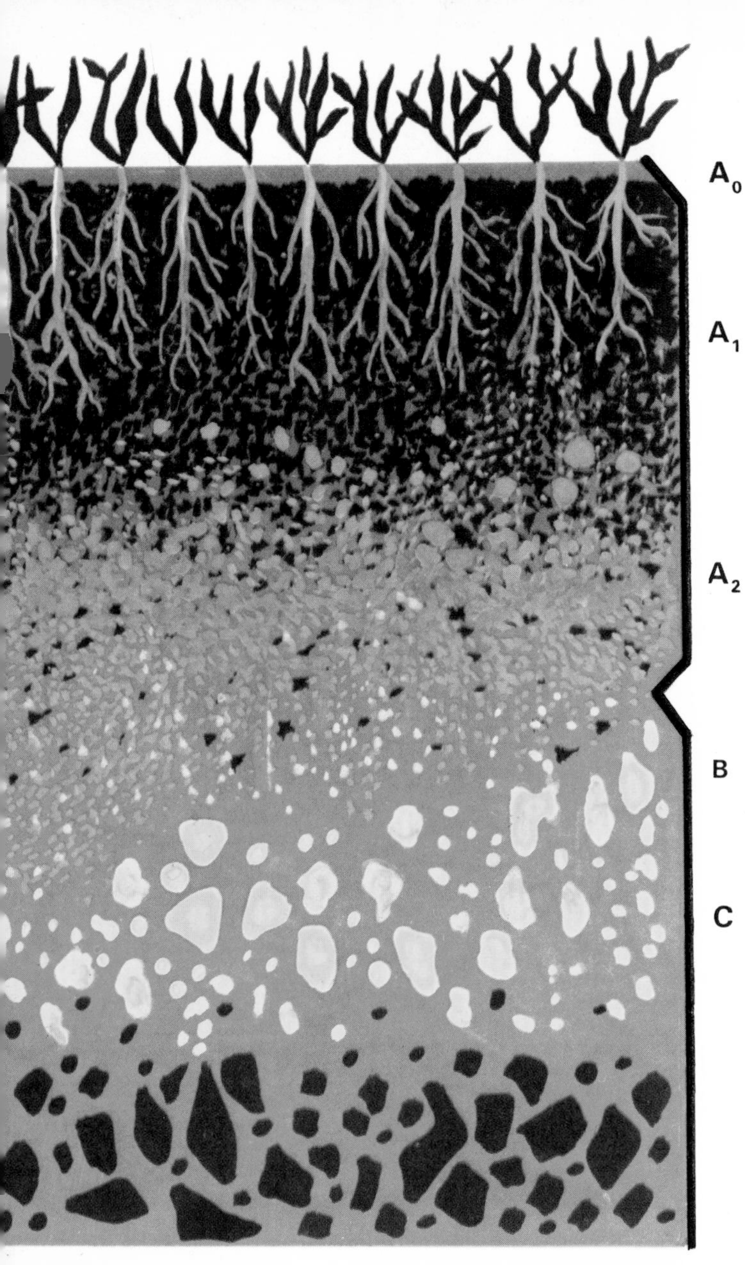

Diagram of grassland soil showing the soil layers and horizons. The litter layer is A0; the humus-rich layer is A1; and the leached topsoil is A2. These make up the A horizon. The B horizon is the subsoil in which leached materials collect. The C horizon is the decomposed material of the parent rock.

or by the vegetation of the plains.

Today the rivers and glaciers, the sea and the wind, are still moving soil and rubble. When a river runs muddied in spate it is carrying soil from one place to another. When the sea erodes a coastline the soil settles as silt on its bed or is deposited on shore or estuary. It has been truly said that there is hardly a square mile of the earth's surface that does not have a little of everywhere else wrapped up in it.

Soil deposited by windblow is known as Loess, and this is the soil of the *steppe* and plains, whether it came from desert or from glacial moraines. Loess from glaciers is found up to ten feet deep, but in China, where it is not of glacial origin, it is up to 2,000 feet deep in places. Trees will grow on loess if there is enough rain, say over 20 inches a year; but loess regions are usually dry or very dry, so are for the most part *steppe* or parkland.

Alluvium is soil that has been moved by water and deposited as silt on flood plains and bottom land. It is fine, close-knit stuff, of the same texture through and through. When a river overflows its banks, then falls back to its old level, leaving mud in the village street, alluvium is what sticks to your boot soles. The flood plains of the Nile and the Yangtse, the Ganges and the Euphrates are alluvial and highly fertile, and it is no accident of history or geography that such places were the sites of early human settlements and civilizations. The ancient Israelites had manna in their wilderness, but it was Pharaoh who had the surplus corn in the Nile delta.

Till is gravel and rubble ground from parent rock, boulder and river bed by the glaciers and left behind after their retreat. Wherever the glaciers moved there are today deposits of till to mark their passage and the end of their trail—from northern Europe to the valleys of the Scottish Highlands and the Canadian Rockies.

Loam is a mixture of sand and clay, kneaded by nature. Peat is composed of undecayed plant matter—alkaline in fens and marshes, acid in upland bogs, as in Scotland, Ireland and the tundra of the north.

Life in the soil

Soil is life, and good soil makes for

variety and wealth of life. Its fertility governs the quality and variety of plants and animals on the ground above. The fertility of soil is more than its structure; it is the sum of its minerals and animals and their related activities, and the activities of the animals and plants above ground.

Minute living things—micro organisms—live in good soil in unbelievable numbers. The weight of bacteria alone is at least a ton to the acre. In every gram of top soil there are 72,000 Amoebae, 62,000 Algae, 111,000 Fungi, and nearly 3 million Actinomycetes, so it is not difficult to believe that the combined weight of microscopic animals below ground is greater than that of all the horses, cows, sheep and rabbits on the surface.

Under natural conditions there is a constant turnover of the nutrients in the soil. Minerals pass from plant to animal when the animal eats the plant. They are then broken down to be used again by plants. Without the decay brought about by fungi and bacteria, minerals would not become locked up in the bodies of animals and plants and lost to the soil. Nitrates, phosphates, and potassium are concentrated in the bodies of animals and plants and are usually scarce in the soil. Their return is therefore necessary if life is to continue.

The minute soil organisms break down dead plants and animals into simple chemicals which can be used again by other plants for growth. Each group of organisms has its specialized job. Some groups convert nitrogen into the nitrates which are essential to plant growth. Other groups tackle dead leaves, others dead animals, and others dead wood. Each does its job of preparing the next stage in the living cycle of the soil.

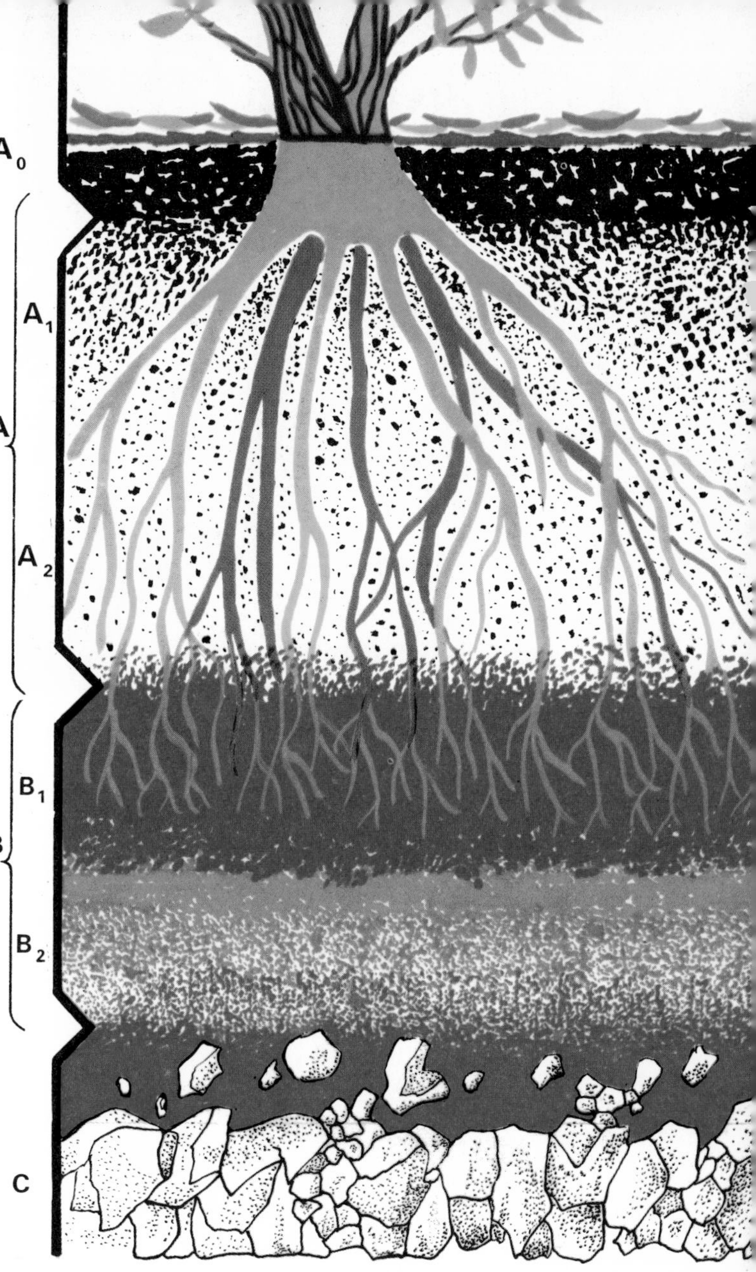

Forest soil showing layers and horizons. Some forest soils leach quickly because of the thin layer of acid humus. The leached materials are therefore washed down quickly into the B horizon where they can be tapped again by the deep roots of the trees. On more alkaline soils which support deciduous forest there is less leaching. Such soils can make good farm-land.

Of all organic materials, wood is the hardest and toughest and the most resistant to decay. Some woods, fortified by natural preservatives like tannin, are even more resistant to attack. But many organisms are specially equipped to assault and break through such fortifications.

Agents of decay

In temperate countries fungi are the first to invade and the most important. They often attack before

In temperate zones fungi are the first agents of decay to attack the defences of trees and may do so long before the trees are dead. Fungi are found in great variety, each species attacking the tree in its own special way.

the tree is dead. These first assault units feed on the sugars and starches of the sap and on the contents of the cells. The blue stains of pine sap-wood are caused by one which attacks cells. The Brown Rot fungi completely destroy simple starches and also the complex ones known as hemi-cellulose. The White Rots destroy cellulose, and lignin which is the hard bony skeleton of wood.

By-products of decay caused by fungi are—water, alcohols, organic acids, esters, aldehydes, carbohydrates, pigments, nitrogenous compounds, anti-bacterial agents and vitamins.

The most obvious immediate effect of fungal decay is that wood becomes light, corky and puffy and absorbs more water. This, together with chemical changes, makes suitable habitats for other organisms; insects.

Insects are second only to fungi in crumbling the defences of wood. Some attack standing trees by boring through the bark into the sap-wood, thus undermining the trees' resistance to attack by fungi. Others attack fallen branches, trunks, stumps, and roots, often in alliance with fungi.

In North America, Europe and Australasia the Powder-Post Beetle bores into seasoned hardwood to reach the sap which its larvae require for growth. This is the extent of its attack but it opens the front to other invading organisms which break through and cause decay.

The European Death-Watch Beetle specializes in boring into hardwood, while a North American species attacks Douglas Fir—a softwood. The Death-Watch can bore into sound timber, but prefers to work where fungi have already caused decay.

Farmers and labourers

Termites are extremely important soil insects in the tropics of Africa, South America, Malaysia and Australasia. They break down wood and other organic matter, and the speed at which wood decays there is due largely to their work. Some species have *protozoa* in their hind gut to help them digest wood; others, with none, eat soil containing vegetable debris. A third group forms a working partnership with fungi, and could be called fungus farmers.

The farmers feed on wood. Much of this is worked on by fungi while it is stored in the termites' humid nest. Early in the rainy season the termites spread the scrapings of fungi combs above ground and these produce mushrooms, which produce spores, which infect organic matter, which is then carried into the nest by the termites, to produce more fungi, to break down more wood for termites.

Economically, termites do a lot of damage to man by eating trees, timber in buildings, cloth, paper, certain crops, and even plastics. Ecologically, they are important to the soil and vital to the maintenance of many habitats.

Some termites live in underground chambers and spend all their lives in the soil. The primitive harvester termites of Africa live below ground but put up little mounds of friable soil on the surface in the way that moles do. Other species build mounds on the surface, sometimes up to 30 feet high. So, whether they live above or below the ground, all termites move soil in some way.

The mound builders carry the soil in their jaws. Some cement the mixture with their saliva. Others, the soil eaters, use their own dung as building material. Yet another group, the wood eaters, construct mounds that are soil on the outside and digested wood on the inside.

Termites that bring soil from a great depth also bring up minerals. If these minerals are already present in the topsoil, the vegetation on the mounds is no different from that surrounding them; if the minerals are different from those present in the topsoil, the vegetation on the mounds becomes different from that surrounding them. This explains why the vegetation of abandoned termite mounds is often quite different from the usual vegetation in the area. It is richer if the subsoil is richer than the topsoil, and poorer if the subsoil is poorer. The termite as mineral borer is sometimes a help to prospectors, because it provides evidence on its mounds of what is below the ground. The soil in many parts of Africa is compacted, and without mineral out-crops to guide the prospector, so the termites save him a lot of fruitless excavation.

Builders and burrowers

On the dry plains of western North America there lives a species of ant that builds a conical mound with soil which it fetches from a great depth below the surface. The earth of these mounds can add up to a weight of 3,400 pounds to the acre. This earth, mixed with organic material, is eventually spread over the surface, thus increasing the depth of topsoil.

Earthworms are great ploughers of the soil. Some species work well below the surface, others among the grass roots. Earthworms eat partly decayed vegetable matter or partly decomposed dung; they also feed on leaves which they pull into their burrows. They digest the soil, refining it and enriching it with their body calcium in the process. As they have to eat a lot of soil to extract the food they need, they pass a great bulk of waste as dung. The worms deposit this dung in the form of casts on the surface, the amount varying from 2 tons per acre a year in a hot dry climate to over 100 tons per acre during the rainy season in the White River Valley of the Sudan. Apart from this turnover of soil by the worms, their burrows aerate and drain it. So the earthworm is an extremely important member of the soil community, even when it irritates man by pulling down the tips of newly

Some termites build mounds up to 30 feet high and these, when deserted, can support a great variety and weight of vegetation. When the termites bring minerals from a great depth they enrich the soil of their mounds. If the minerals brought up by the termites are different from those found nearer the surface, the vegetation on the mounds may be quite different from that surrounding them.

The Common Shrew of Europe is a small insectivorous mammal. It hunts round the clock, mainly in the leaf litter which can be seen heaving when the shrew is working. It is a voracious feeder and eats at least its own body weight every day.

planted vegetables such as leeks.

Burrowing mammals like foxes, badgers, prairie dogs, gophers and ground squirrels, although not part of the actual soil community, work in the soil and make their presence felt. Gophers and ground squirrels, for example, can move 30 to 40 tons of soil on an acre in a few months. The mole turns over soil by putting up moleheaps, and its tunnels help to aerate and drain it. Mice, voles and rabbits also burrow, and where-ever there are burrows there are entries for air and water.

The Aardvark, or Ant-bear, is a specialist predator on termites. It is found in Africa from the Cape to Abyssinia, the Sudan and Senegal. The name aardvark was given it by Dutch settlers and means earth-pig. It is about the size of a pig. The claws of its fore-feet are big and powerful and used for digging.

Humus—the heart of soil

Humus is the name given to the decomposed animal and vegetable matter in soil—its decayed organic content. Although the creation of humus is mainly the work of bacteria, the earthworm plays a big part in reducing organic matter to humus—which is why a mature, rich soil has plenty of earthworms. Humus holds moisture in the soil, and insulates it against extremes of temperature. The amount of humus present varies from 1 per cent in poor soil to 20 per cent in good, fertile soil.

Peat is undecayed vegetable matter and therefore not humus. Added to the soil it can be turned into humus by the action of bacteria and earthworms. Decomposition is extremely slow in water-logged peat—so slow in fact that the pollen of trees has been preserved down through the ages in successive layers to tell the plant history of the area.

In temperate regions the rate of decomposition is severely limited by temperature. In the tropics decomposition is extremely rapid. On savannas organic matter rarely lasts for more than a few hours or days. A heap of elephant dung, three feet deep, can be demolished by dung beetles within a few hours. In the Scottish Highlands, by contrast, deer droppings can persist for up to two years on the cold hills and still be recognizable as deer droppings.

Just a trace

Some soils, with every appearance of fertility, still cannot grow good crops, and this may be due to a lack of elements in the soil which are required by plants in only the minutest quantities. These are the so-called Trace Elements, like manganese, copper, iron, cobalt and iodine. A trace of these applied to a soil that is short of them, makes all the difference between infertility and fertility.

Many soils are short of one or other of the trace elements at any given time. Such shortages are common and widespread in Australia and to some extent in New Zealand. In both countries the soil has been brought into production by application of the missing elements—a famous example being the Ninety Mile Desert in South Australia, which is now an experimental farming region.

Minerals in soil can be washed or dissolved away by rain. Leaching is the action of rain when it carries minerals in solution from the topsoil to lower levels. All soils lose minerals to some extent by leaching. Humus-rich soils are leached slowly because humus holds moisture and therefore traps the minerals in solution; so, while there is some loss, there is also a saving for the use of plants.

The European Mole tunnels under the soil, hunting for earthworms and other soil animals. Its main food is earthworms. This is the animal responsible for the well-known mole heaps seen on pastures.

Grasslands leach slowly because they are rich in humus. The same is true of the best arable soils kept in good heart by good husbandry. Some forest soils leach quickly because of the thin top layer of humus. The topsoil under this layer, being short of humus, is deficient in minerals, which are washed lower down.

There is a general relationship of soil to quality of vegetation and to the abundance, size, variety, health and vigour of animal life in the ecosystem.

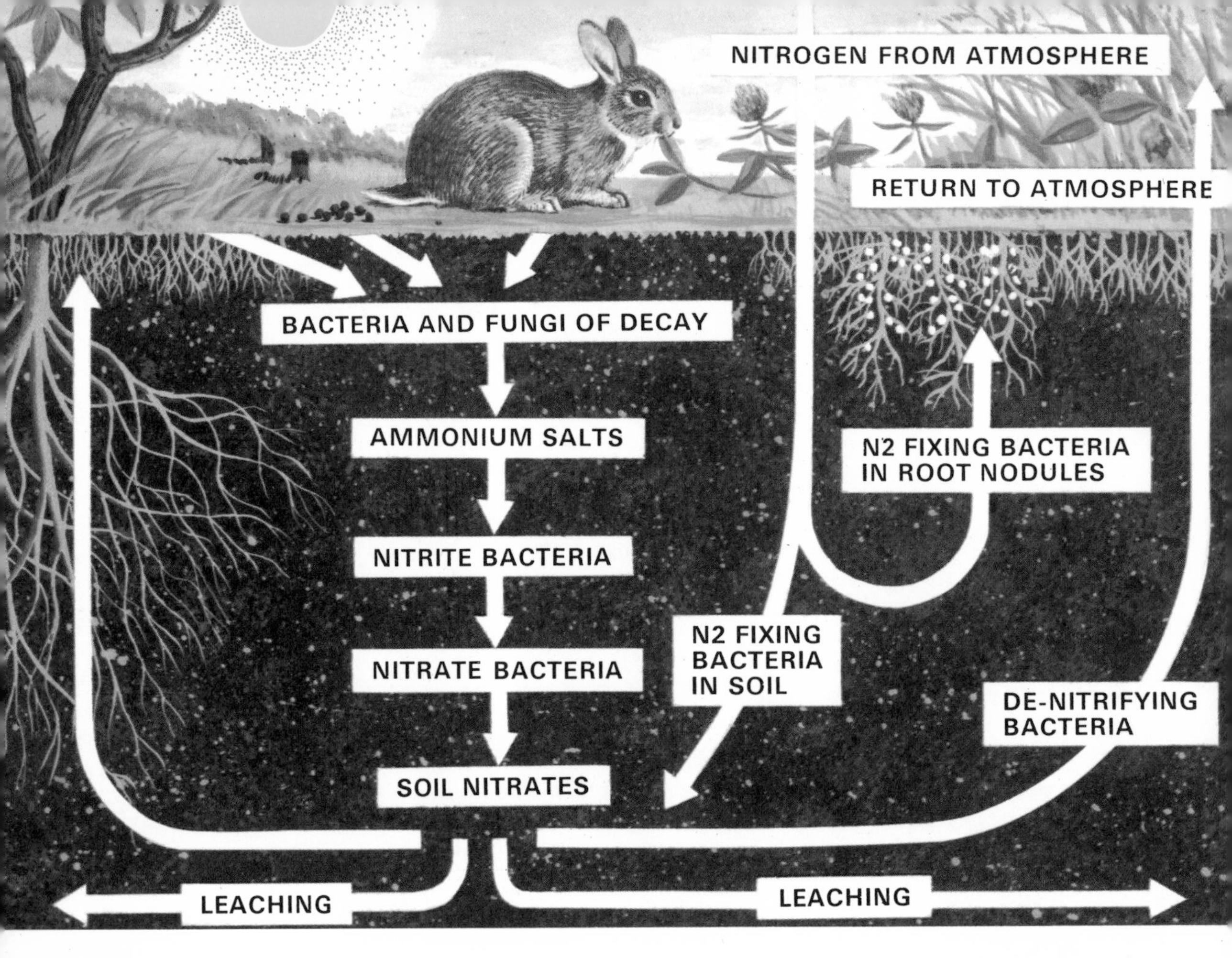

Mineral Cycle. Minerals are taken from the soil by the roots of plants. Animals obtain their minerals from the plants. When plants and animals die their minerals are returned to the soil.

Hydrologic Cycle. Water is returned to the atmosphere by evaporation—from open water and from the leaves of plants. Some is also returned by transpiration from plants.

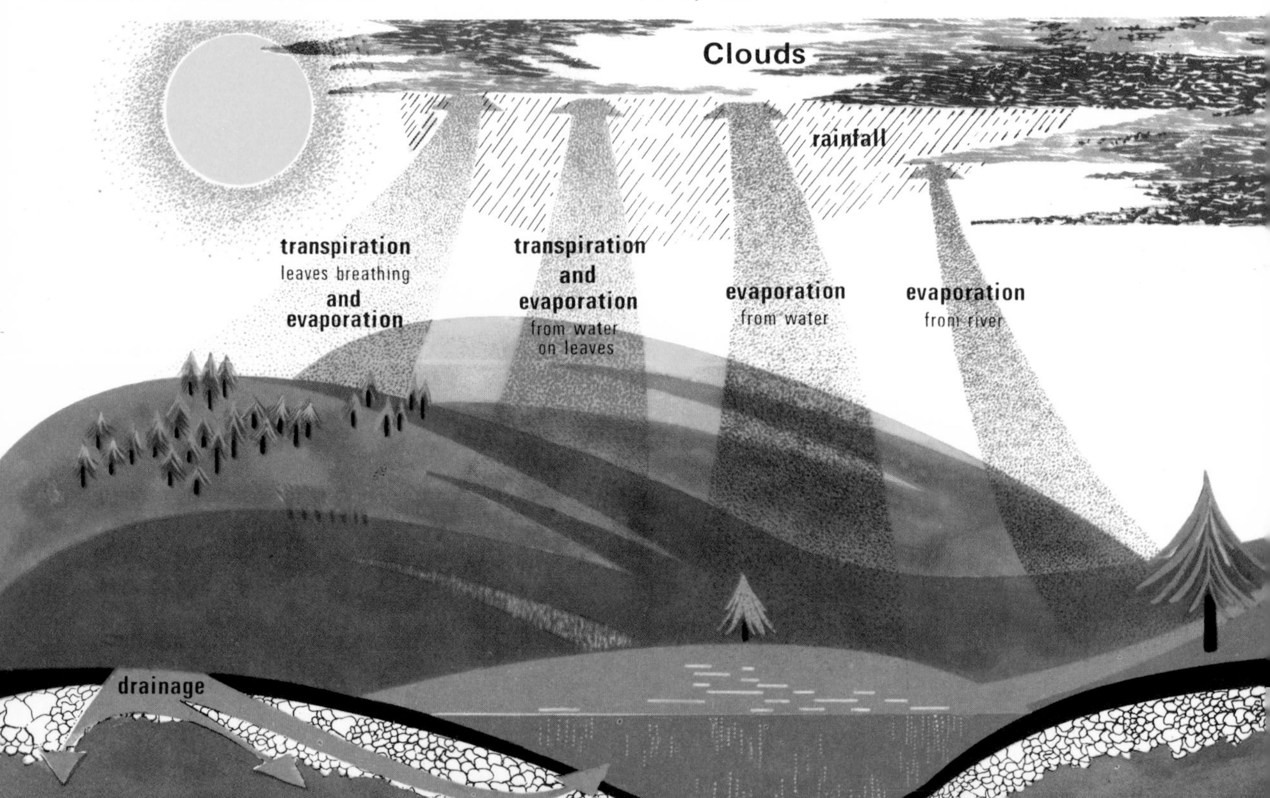

—is deriving energy at three removes from the source.

There is thus a stage by stage transfer of energy—from plant to animal, and from one animal to another. But there is a loss of energy all along the line and at each transfer. A vole that eats 23 pounds of grass in six months weighs hardly more than an ounce at the end of the period. A fox that eats 16 mice is 16 mice heavier at the end of the meal, but may not be a mouse heavier by the end of the day.

Although green plants are the sole distributors of energy to all other living things, they use only a small fraction of the sun's available energy—a hundredth to a twentieth—for this purpose. The remainder of the sun's energy is expended in other ways—by reflection from vegetation, rocks or water; in heating the air and the soil; and in evaporation of water from pools, rivers, lakes and sea. As warmth it affects the living conditions of plants and animals in a variety of ways.

The flow of the sun's energy into the ecosystem is one-way traffic. It is also subject to constant loss in its transfer from plants to a succession of animals. So there has to be constant replenishment from the sun—its only source.

Cycles of minerals

The flow of minerals is different—a circuit instead of a one-way street. The minerals are taken up by the roots of plants, and used for growth. When an animal eats a plant it obtains minerals from the leafage. When some other animal eats the plant-eater it obtains its minerals from the prey. During an animal's lifetime it returns some of the minerals in the form of dung, which is broken down by dung beetles or weathering. After the animal dies, its body is broken down and its minerals released by the soil chemists among the bacteria. If the body is partly eaten by a scavenger, the return of the minerals in that part is delayed.

Once the minerals have been freed in the soil the process begins all over again—to plant root and plant, thence along the animal chain, and back to earth as before. But the soil has other mineral sources, the most obvious one being the parent rock—a source that can be tapped only by deep-rooted plants and trees. Soil bacteria can trap free nitrogen from the upper air and turn it into the nitrates needed by plants as food. Other bacteria found in the root nodules of plants like clover, lucerne (alfalfa), lupin, pea, and alder, also produce nitrates from the ammonias in the soil.

Minerals can be brought up by springs to produce local flushes of vegetation, and can be carried to lower ground by streams flowing over outcrops of parent rock. In forests, 'where much of the soil's mineral output is tied up for long periods in the trees, there is an annual return from leaf-fall in the autumn. This is so with deciduous trees. In coniferous forest, where there is a continuous fall of needles, the breakdown is slower.

Minerals lost to an ecosystem by leaching may be carried by rivers to the sea, from which they may eventually be brought back to land in the guano of sea birds, to be spread on farms as fertilizer. But it is unlikely that they are ever returned to the ecosystem that lost them.

The water cycle

All life needs water, so all life is

dependent on rain. The rain drains into the soil where it becomes water available to plants. It drains deeper to feed underground springs, and is brought by them to the surface again. It enters streams and rivers by falling into them, by draining into them, and running off the land surface into them, and is carried to the sea. It is returned to the atmosphere by evaporation and transpiration. It evaporates from pools, puddles, streams, rivers and the sea. It evaporates from the leaves of trees, from rocks and herbage, and while it is actually falling. It is given back by trees and plants by transpiration and by animals during respiration. Much water, locked up in plant and animal bodies during their lifetime, is freed when they die.

Apart from drinking it, man uses water for a great variety of purposes—irrigation, power and industrial processes—and his demand for it increases year by year. To man it is more than life; it makes possible his present way of life.

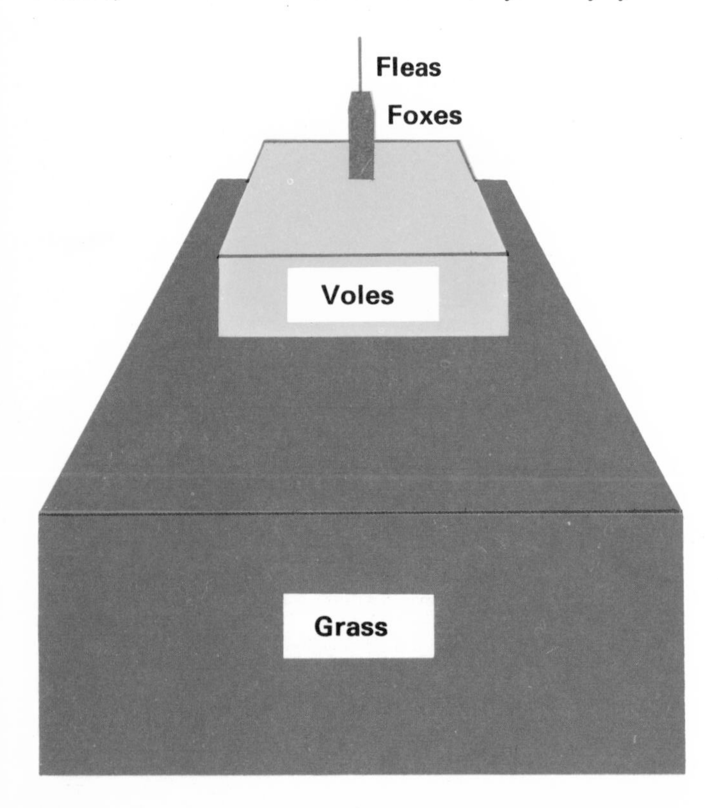

Pyramid illustrating the relationship between grass, voles and foxes on 1,000 acres of recently planted forest. Five million pounds of grass maintained 6,250 pounds of voles and 14 pounds of fox. The vole population was 100 per acre. The pyramid shows the weight of animals produced, and the loss of energy through the food chain from grass to vole to fox to the flea on the fox (after Nigel Charles).

Pyramids

An ecosystem is like man's social organization in many ways—with each unit occupying its appointed place, doing its appointed job, behaving in a proper manner and standing in some sort of relationship to every other unit.

The flow of energy from plant to animal, and from one animal to another, creates a relationship between eater and eaten and fixes the order of eating. The order of eating is plant to plant-eater, to meat-eater, perhaps to a second meat-eater, then to parasite or scavenger. They are like the links in a chain.

A Food Chain is the sequence of plant eaten by caterpillar eaten by small bird eaten by hawk eaten by eagle tormented by fleas. So is grass eaten by a grasshopper eaten by a mouse eaten by a weasel eaten by the fox with the flea in his ear. So are green algae eaten by a shrimp eaten by a trout eaten by a pike caught by a fisherman. Man, who eats a great variety of foods from many parts of the world, is at the end of many food chains.

Food chains can become webs. Plant to vole to weasel makes a chain. But voles are also eaten by foxes, stoats, hawks, owls and crows. Foxes and owls sometimes kill weasels. Foxes kill owlets. Crows eat the eggs of owls and sometimes eat owlets. Thus a web is woven, often of great intricacy.

One way of looking at an ecosystem is to examine the total weight of life it can support: that is its Biomass. The weight of plant life is the product of sun and soil, and plants supply the ecosystem with its total energy. The weight of plants is therefore greater than that

of all the animals added together. As some energy is lost at each link in the food chain, there will be a greater weight of first line carnivores than of second line carnivores and a greater weight of second line carnivores than of parasites on them.

Suppose a fox were to live entirely on field voles for a year. He would require 5475 voles. Each vole eats 50 pounds of grass. This means that voles have to eat 122 tons of grass to supply one fox with energy for a year—a fox weighing perhaps 18 pounds. Of course, the fox would not really be living entirely on voles; he would be eating other grass-eaters as well. But the end result would be the same. By comparison, a herbivore like the roebuck, three times the weight of the fox, eats only about half a ton of green food a year. The loss of energy through the food chain to the fox is almost incredibly greater than that from plant to roebuck.

Each in its proper place

A species living in its proper place, behaving in the proper way, and doing its proper job, is said to be occupying its proper Ecological Niche, which means that its relationship to other species and to the ecosystem as a whole is correct.

So we can speak of Feeding, Breeding and Roosting Niches—where the species best suited to the system finds the best conditions for itself. Some species—rat and mouse come readily to mind—are adaptable, and can move into other niches and do well. Others, less adaptable, have to stay where they are. In a properly balanced ecosystem everything is in its proper niche.

Sea birds that nest on cliffs have their special nesting niches. Kittiwake gulls nest on sheer faces, on

The Kittiwake is a member of the gull family that nests on sea cliffs which it shares with other species like gannets, guillemots and razorbills. But although sea birds appear, at first glance, to be mixed up on a cliff face they have in fact their own places, or niches, there. Kittiwakes use the smallest ledges, just big enough to hold a nest. Even when hunting the kittiwake exploits its particular niche in the sea and dives for its living.

Gannets nest on sea cliffs in large colonies. The world population of gannets is presently estimated at 250,000.

The European Chaffinch lives in mixed woodlands all over Europe but not in pine woods where the Blue Chaffinch is present.

shelves hardly bigger than a man's hand. Guillemots nest on sloping ledges, razorbills in recesses, puffins in burrows and herring gulls on grassy slopes on the cliff top. Cormorants nest at the base.

When these birds go fishing out at sea they separate into different feeding niches, either by going to different places or hunting in different ways. The herring gull hunts inland and along the shoreline; the kittiwake feeds out at sea and dives for its living. Guillemots, razorbills, puffins and cormorants are all divers, but they hunt different kinds of fish most of the time.

After the breeding season they tend to separate into different parts of the ocean. Separation in these three ways means that they all use the ecosystem differently most of the time, so they are hardly ever in competition with each other.

The European chaffinch is found in broad-leaved and coniferous woodlands all over Europe, but is much more at home in broad-leaved. In the Canary Islands, where it comes up against the blue chaffinch, it is not found in pine woods if the blue is present. There the blue holds the niche. In pine woods where there are no blues the European species takes over and occupies the niche.

Two African woodpeckers behave in the same way. There is a woodpecker of dry country and one of rain forest, and the two are never found together. But the dry country woodpecker is found in one isolated montane rain forest from which the other is absent. The dry country species can occupy the rain forest niche, but is only able to do so when the other is not there.

The lions, leopards, wild dogs and cheetahs of Zambia's Kafue National Park prey on about 20 species of wild, hoofed animals, or

The Cape Hunting Dog, or African Wild Dog, hunts in packs.

ungulates. Although these hunters spread their killing over all the prey species, each tends to kill hardest what the others kill least, or to a much lesser extent. Here each occupies a niche while retaining some freedom of movement.

Wild ungulates avoid competition in a variety of ways. In the Tarangire Game Reserve, Tanzania, about 20 species find a living without getting in each other's way. They manage this by living in different parts of the ecosystem, eating different kinds of food, feeding on vegetation at different heights, occupying different areas at the same season or the same areas at different seasons.

Giraffes are the tallest animals—up to 18 feet in total height.

Rose-bay willow-herb, meadow-sweet, and young hawthorns in possession of ground formerly covered by mixed woodland of pines and hardwoods felled during the Second World War. Meadow-sweet grows in the damp hollows; the rose-bay takes over where the ground has been bared. Rose-bay also colonizes after fire, its other name being Fireweed. These are early plants in the forest succession.

And all together

Animal and plant communities do not grow together overnight; they need time. A forest that is felled does not grow into what it was at the first try, nor within a few years. It does so by stages. The series of stages is called a *Succession*. When the last stage is reached, in this case forest, it is called a *Climax*.

Every ecosystem has its succession and its natural climax. In some the succession has many stages; in others there are few. The chain of succession from bare rock to climax forest has many links: lichens, communities of mosses and ferns, annual grasses, perennial grasses, shrubs, pioneer trees, pines and climax hardwoods. At each stage there is a distinctive animal community. Together they prepare the way for the next stage. In the end there is climax forest with its associated plant and animal communities.

By contrast the succession to a tundra community is a short chain —lichens, sedges and grasses. This is a simple climax of few plant species, and the animal community is also one of few species.

The early stages of a succession are, in a way, like the first anchoring strands of a spider's web. Break any one, or all, and the spider has to begin again. But break a few strands of the completed web and it will still hold together while the spider gets on with the repairs.

Climax is like that—insulated against extremes of climate, able to cope with the ravages of nature, quick in healing over the scars of fire, storm or disease. Its strength and resilience—its stability in fact—lie in its variety, and the cooperative working of its parts. Greatest stability lies in great variety, because not all parts of the whole are at risk to the same threat at the same time, and one part often shields another.

A break in the succession towards natural climax can be caused in a number of ways.

Fire and arrest

Fire is one way. If burning is light, the clock may be set back only a little; heavy burning can set it far back, even to the beginning. Fire, natural or man-made, is such a constant hazard in certain places that the natural climax is never reached. The succession is arrested indefinitely. This is a *Fire Climax*.

Ever since he discovered fire, man has used it for a variety of purposes, often with care, just as often carelessly. It is one of the weapons he uses to control certain environments, to arrest natural succession at a stage that suits him, to produce in fact a man-made climax. He holds the succession at this stage by regular use of fire.

In the Canadian barrens, fire can turn a habitat suitable for caribou into one suited to moose. The caribou feed on lichens in the winter, and find them in the Taiga climax of spruce and pine. Fire destroys the climax community, and puts it back to a stage where willows and poplars become abundant and lichens scarce. This favours moose at the expense of caribou.

In Scotland the world-famous grouse moors are a fire climax, held at the heather stage by man in the interests of a game bird—the red grouse. In other parts of Scotland, a combination of fire and grazing by sheep and deer holds the succession back from its natural climax of pine and oak forest.

Grazing animals, wild or domestic, can hold a succession at a grassland climax. In the Murchison Falls National Park, Uganda, elephants have become so numerous that they have destroyed the woodland climax, and now hold the succession at grassland.

The aim of almost all man's activities on the land is to arrest succession at a stage that suits him. If he didn't do this there would be no farming. Grain, potatoes, vegetables, fruit and hay grow because man arranges the environment for them by farming. If a farm is deserted nature soon begins to take over, and sets the succession going again towards climax. It does not take long for even the wheel ruts to become overgrown with weeds.

The Wheatear is a common bird of hillside and moorland where there are outcrops of rock. In Scotland it is numerous where ground has been heavily burned or grazed, because burning and grazing by causing erosion and baring the rocks help to create the kind of habitat the wheatear prefers. It nests under rocks, in rocky crevices, or in ground burrows.

CHAPTER 3

TUNDRA

Below the polar ice cap the tundra zone straggles round the neck of the world in coastal strip and land mass and scatter of islands—a harsh, treeless Arctic terrain of short summers and incalculable winter cold.

Although it is, ecologically, a simple zone, its simplicity is not uniform. The variety of plant and animal communities increases from north to south.

The most northerly strip, as in coastal Alaska, is the most simple. Southwards, like a ripple spreading, this gives way to swamps known as muskegs, then to lichened woodlands of stunted trees, then to taller trees, then to the zone of coniferous forest that wraps the shoulders of the world like a cape.

There is a similar increase in variety of animal species, although this is not the same right round the tundra zone. Frank Pitelka lists seven mammal species on the coastal tundra of Alaska—two shrews, two lemmings, two foxes, and the least weasel.

Thirty miles inland the number becomes 11—the additions being the ground squirrel, the tundra vole, the short-tailed weasel and the caribou.

Eighty-five miles inland the number increases to 17—the additions being the moose, the wolverine, the grizzly bear, the wolf and two species of vole. The coyote, the tundra hare and the hoary marmot, are found occasionally in the third line.

The number of bird species on the same lines is 22, 24 and 32.

At the bottom of the world, in the Antarctic, the ice cap covers almost the entire land surface, so that tundra hardly exists, and where it does it is little more than bare rock or primitive lichens, void of animal life. There the native animals find their living in the sea.

In some parts of the world, far from the Arctic, high mountain plateaux provide a tundra climate with tundra vegetation and animal life. This is alpine tundra—the product of altitude instead of latitude. The greatest area of alpine tundra in the world is the high Tibetan plateau. Similar, but smaller areas occur in the Alps and Carpathian Mountains of Europe and in the Andes of South America.

The Arctic tundra is wet, cold wasteland, where snowfall mostly replaces rainfall and where the ground is permanently frozen to within a short distance of the surface—the Permafrost. The cold means that there is hardly any loss of moisture by evaporation and the ice barrier just under the surface means there is little loss by down drainage. So, despite the light snowfall, amounting to no more than the

The Caribou of the North American tundra is known in Europe as the Reindeer.

Alpine grassland over 3,500 feet in the Cairngorm Mountains of Scotland. At this altitude, climate and terrain resemble Arctic tundra. Grass is often replaced by moss-heaths or junipers. Snow often lies in patches into mid-summer or later.

The Short-tailed Vole of Europe is found on moorland and hillsides as well as in young plantations. It lives in simple habitats of few plant species, often in conditions resembling tundra, where it can reach plague numbers.

equivalent of one to ten inches of rain a year, the water is held near the surface which remains wet in summer and freezes over in winter. The ice barrier also means that there is hardly any loss of minerals by leaching.

The tundra winter is long and cold, with day and night linked in darkness; the summer is short and warm. The vegetation grows quickly. It has to make a year's growth in a few weeks, to support the animals that feed on it. Tundra vegetation is short or prostrate—grasses, sedges, lichens and berry-bearing shrubs—and is soon covered by protecting snow in winter.

Residents and travellers

Some animals spend the whole of their lives in this harsh environment; others, especially birds, move out and back. Lemmings, voles and weasels live most of the winter under the snow. Ptarmigan burrow in it. Only the ground squirrels hibernate in the true sense. Bears spend part of the long winter denned up under the snow, in a kind of waking sleep, living on their fat, and give birth to their cubs during this period. The caribou, the musk ox, the Arctic fox, and the wolf have to keep on the move and make the best of it.

The caribou of the Canadian barrens move southwards into the lichened woodlands or taiga, north of the great forest belt, and their migrations are part of history. These great herds, feeding as they move through the barren lands, are shadowed by the wolf packs, and young, old and diseased animals are pulled down and eaten. Other predators like the wolverine and the bear, attack the herds. But the migration of the caribou goes on

Norwegian lemming. This is the species whose mass emigrations have captured the popular imagination and whose behaviour has become encrusted with legend. Emigration is movement of a large part of the population from an overcrowded home range.

until they have reached their destination. In the spring they make their return journey, backtracking along their winter route, when they are again followed by the wolves whose movements are very much tied to theirs.

The caribou of Greenland, Spitzbergen and Baffin Island have to stick it out on their summer range.

The musk ox, which is as big as a pony, roams the tundra the year round, usually in groups of a family of two, rarely in bigger herds. When threatened by a wolf pack the musk ox form a defensive phalanx, presenting their brow shields of heavy flat horn to the enemy. But no defence is perfect and the wolves sometimes win.

Wolverine—also known as the Glutton or Indian Devil. This is the most powerful member of the weasel family.

The Polar Bear, which hunts the Arctic pack ice, is the biggest land carnivore in existence, weighing up to 1,600 pounds.

Fat and lean

Bears lay on fat to see them through the inactive period, drawing on it for their own body needs and to produce milk for their cubs. Foxes and wolves put on fat too, but they are active hunters right through the winter and would not survive for long on their fat reserves alone. Laying on fat in times of plenty is a help to all the tundra animals in the lean days ahead.

Foxes, ermines, hawks and snowy owls prey on lemmings, voles and ptarmigan. If the voles and lemmings eat all the berries the ptarmigan suffer and become scarcer. Caribou can be hit in the same way and some may die of starvation, thus providing food for scavenging wolves, bears and ravens. When lemmings and voles themselves become scarce, the hunters have to thin out or move out; they return when their prey becomes plentiful again.

So, on the tundra, as anywhere else, the hunters have to adjust their numbers to the food supply;

The Snowy Owl of the tundra is one of the main predators on the teeming lemmings.

Musk Oxen remain on the same range throughout the year. Cows give birth to their calves at two-year intervals.

The Greylag Goose is a sociable bird at nesting time. It breeds on moors, reed beds, marshes and islets, in Arctic Scandinavia, the Baltic States and North Russia as well as locally farther south in Europe. The Northern birds move south for the winter.

mouths have to be kept related to mouthfuls. Everything is dependent in some way on everything else. Snowy owls vary their egg output according to the lemming supply, laying from three to six in poor years, and up to a dozen or more in good ones. Even human beings are affected. When the lemmings eat all the crow-berries the Eskimos have to do without, and as a result suffer from a disease due to vitamin deficiency.

Few people have adapted themselves to life in the tundra. In North

The Ermine is the stoat in winter dress. The change from summer-brown to winter-white is the result of a moult.

The Red-throated Diver nests on the shores of small lochs close to the water's edge in northern Scotland, Iceland, Scandinavia and North Russia.

America the Eskimos have done so. One race lives on the coastal tundra and depends mainly on seals for food and clothing. Another race lives inland on the Canadian barrens, and depends on caribou. The hunters intercept the animals on the north and south migrations. In northern Europe the Lapps have domesticated the caribou, which they call the reindeer, and depend on it for venison, milk and clothing. But they have to move with the migrating animals, and so have become part nomads themselves.

CHAPTER 4

DESERTS

Deserts have a low rainfall, high temperatures, and rapid loss of moisture by evaporation. Examples are the Sahara of endless sand and rock; the great deserts of Australia; the parched Chilean barrens where no plants grow; the arid burning wastes of Arabia; the Sonora of Mexico; the Mojave of cactus and creosote bush and the Great Basin of sage brush in the southwest U.S.A.

Deserts are not all alike; nor are all the parts of any one of them. Some parts get rain at intervals; others get it all at once; yet others get no rain for a year or more at a time.

Rainfall in the Sahara varies from zero to 10 inches a year, so at its highest it equals that of the tundra; yet the tundra is permanently wet while the Sahara is almost permanently dry. But the tundra is cold with hardly any evaporation, while the Sahara is hot with almost total evaporation.

High temperature and low rainfall mean parched soil and scant vegetation. This means that there is hardly any organic decay, which means that little humus is added to the soil, which is therefore starved of nitrogen. On the other hand there is hardly any leaching of minerals. If water can be brought by irrigation a desert can be made to bloom, so long as there are no harmful salts in the ground. This has been achieved on a great scale in Israel.

Sand deserts become hot on the surface by day, but lose heat quickly to the cloudless sky at night. Rock deserts, by contrast, absorb heat by day and retain most of it at night, so that the temperature remains high round the clock. Noon summer temperature in the Sahara can be as high as 130 degrees Fahrenheit; more usually it is about 110 degrees. The fall at night ranges from 15 to 75 degrees. In the Great Basin of Nevada, U.S.A. the night drop in winter can bring frost.

Much thirst and little water

Some plants and animals have to stay near whatever water there is, others can live in the open desert far away from it.

Where rain falls heavily at long intervals it soaks deeply into hollows, which means there is no loss by evaporation. In such places plants can grow. Typical of these are the Sahara oases of date palms, Terebinth and acacias. In the Sonora Desert the giant Saguaros, with their dwarf underlay of Cholla cacti are replaced at washes by Acacias, Mesquites, Ironwoods and Palo Verdes (literally Green Sticks) —all of them with long tap roots reaching deep for water and giving away as little as possible through

Mexican desert with cacti near the Sierra Madre del Sur.

their small leaves. The Creosote bush of the Mojave sends its roots forty feet deep. The Saguaro can take in a ton of water during rain and make it last for four years if need be.

Plants of the open desert have to collect and store as much water as they can during the infrequent rain. Then they have to part with as little as possible by transpiration—which is much the same as an animal losing moisture by breath and sweat.

Water can be stored in roots or underground tubers. The wide spreading roots of the Saguaro gather water during a rainstorm and the whole plant swells up. Loss of water is slowed by the plants having leaves with a waxy covering, tightly rolled to reduce drying by the wind, or by having no leaves at all—like cacti. The green stem of the cactus plant acts as leafage in capturing the sun's energy.

Some desert animals depend on plants for water as well as food, and the plants have evolved defences of thorns or spikes with a bitter taste, an unpleasant smell, or even a poisonous secretion. Of course these defences are successful only in part; otherwise there would be no desert animals. The animals eat part of the plant, and in so doing deplete its water reserve, but they do not kill it. This is another example of a balance being struck —between the plant's ability to protect itself and the animal's forcefulness in getting what it needs.

Cooling down

Like the plants, the desert animals have to conserve water or they would soon dry up. One way of doing this is to keep out of the sun as much as possible, and one way of getting out of the sun is to burrow in the ground. When the outside temperature is 106 degrees Fahrenheit, the temperature two feet down a burrow is 80 degrees, and the moisture in such burrows is three or four times greater than above ground.

It is no accident therefore that burrowing animals are more common in deserts than anywhere else. If we compare forests and grass prairies with deserts we find that—

In forest one animal out of sixteen is a burrower.

On grass prairie one animal out of two is a burrower.

On desert three animals out of four are burrowers.

Rodents are common animals in deserts and all of them are burrowers. Burrowing helps them to escape from their enemies; it also lets them escape from the hot sun. Keeping out of the sun is a way of keeping cool, and keeping cool is a way of saving body water. The whistling rats of the Kalahari Desert are burrowers. So are the jerboas of the Sahara. And the kangaroo rats and wood rats of the American southwest. The pocket mouse of the Sonora desert will stay in its burrow for days at a time when the sun is too hot.

But rodents are not the only burrowers in the desert. Lizards do so when the sun threatens to heat them above danger level; they also do so to escape their enemies. Frogs and toads burrow for the same reasons. The aardwolf and the honey badger of the Kalahari Desert are burrowers. Saharan burrowers are the fox, the fennec fox and the desert cat.

Coming out at night, whatever other advantages it may have, is another way of keeping cool. Many rodents do it. The jerboas of the Sahara come out only at night and plug up the entrance to their burrows during the day. The kangaroo rats, wood rats and jackrabbits of the American deserts are nocturnal.

Drinkers and non-drinkers

Every species has to come to terms with desert conditions and with other species in the best way it can. Apart from keeping cool, the main problems are getting water and holding on to it.

The most obvious way of taking in water is to drink it straight but this is not easy in the desert where permanent waterholes are few and far between. Nevertheless some animals have to do it. The desert bighorn sheep of America is one; it will travel many miles to water then drink enough to last it for several days. The sand grouse of North Africa and Asia are the same and have to live within flying distance of water.

Birds of prey get all the water they need from the animals they eat; but mammal carnivores have to drink sometimes, even if it is at long intervals, and so are tied to the neighbourhood of permanent or temporary waterholes.

At the other extreme the kangaroo rat of American deserts has practically freed itself from dependence on water; it gets all it needs from the dry seeds it eats—partly from the small amount of water they contain and partly by manufacturing more during digestion. The gerbils of the Sahara also do this and can live on seeds containing as little as 10 per cent of water.

Between these two groups are animals that depend for their water on juicy vegetation—cacti for example. The pack rats of the U.S.A. and the sand rats of Africa get their water in this fashion; the Americans get theirs from succulent leafage.

The Kangaroo Rat—equipped by nature to extract water from the driest of food and to make maximum use of the water it extracts.

The mole lemmings of Asia get their water from the bulbs of wild tulips.

Surprisingly, toads and frogs can live in deserts, especially toads with their dry skin. But they need actual water to breed in. They appear after rain and lay their eggs in rain pools. The eggs soon hatch, the tadpoles grow quickly, and growth to legged toad and frog is completed before

The Jerboa is a rodent of deserts and steppes, known in North Africa as the Desert Rat. It is nocturnal in habits.

The Leaf-tailed Gecko. Geckos have a vertical eye pupil.

the pools dry up. Newts, on the other hand, cannot live in deserts because they need water all the time.

Of all the backboned animals lizards are the most completely suited to living in deserts. They get all the water they need from their prey. No moisture is lost through their skin, which is waterproof and leathery. Their body wastes are passed almost dry and solid, the water content having been largely extracted beforehand for re-use.

Big hoofed animals—camels, asses, gazelles, oryxes, addaxes, bighorns—have to drink water sometimes and conserve it between times. The camel can go for long periods without water, then it replaces the loss at one long draught. Between times it uses water slowly, drawing on the fatty reserves in its hump, which becomes water by body chemistry. A fatty deposit of 66 pounds provides about 70 pints of water. The camel loses nothing by sweating. Instead, its body becomes a sort of storage heater, warming up by day and giving off heat at night. Its kidneys extract water from urine for re-use, as in the case of the kangaroo rats of America. In addition to all this the camel can extract the maximum amount of water from the driest food.

The addax antelope of the Sahara can also live on the driest vegetation

A Camel Caravan. Camels were introduced from Asia to North Africa. In the desert the camel is a draught animal, and means of transport.

and go without water for long periods. It has, of course, no hump. Gazelles and wild asses can also go for long spells without water. And they have no humps. But in some way, not yet understood, they must be able to store and conserve water as the camel does.

Some desert animals become torpid in the hottest season or when food is scarce. Snakes and lizards, being cold blooded, are forced to retreat underground when the temperature becomes too high. Some warm-blooded animals do the same. Rock squirrels have such an inactive period. The Mojave ground squirrel can lie up in its burrow for many months without food or water, not always asleep, but never coming out. This withdrawal period is called aestivation, summer instead of winter sleep, during which the body works slow down and energy is used up at a greatly reduced rate. It is as near death as it is possible for an animal to get without actually dying.

The Addax is one of the world's threatened species but is still illegally hunted even where it is protected by law. In Ancient Egypt it was kept as a domestic animal for its meat.

The Oasis of Tozeur, in Tunisia. Oases are green places in the desert where there is a constant supply of water. The date palm is a characteristic tree of North African oases.

CHAPTER 5

GRASSLANDS AND SAVANNAS

The world's natural grasslands lie between the great forest and desert belts—a thick sandwich between wet and dry. They have a rainfall of about 15 inches a year—too high for desert, not high enough to produce enduring forest. Where rainfall is much less than this, desert begins to take over; where it is greater the grass begins to give way to shrubs and trees.

All grasslands have a great variety of grasses, but the variety is not the same in all of them. Tall, medium or short, the grasses are all deep-rooted. Tall grasses are found in the wetter parts, short ones in drier parts. The prairies of America are tall grass regions; the short grasses grow on the plains. Flowering plants are usually mixed with the grasses. Low rainfall and abundant soil humus mean that there is little leaching of minerals, so grasslands are generally rich and productive.

The world's grasslands once carried great herds of wild animals but man has slaughtered most of them to make way for domestic cattle and sheep, and for farming.

The bison of the North American plains, once 50 million strong, have been reduced to a few thousand head. The great herds that migrated across the prairies like an army, making the earth tremble with the thunder of their hoofs, were the prey of the Red Man. They provided him with meat, hides and bones. They were his geese that laid the golden eggs, and his predation never at any time threatened their numbers. The coming of the white man changed all that and with the building of the railroads the appalling slaughter began. Helpless, the Indians stood by while their livelihood was destroyed.

The bison were massacred to feed the railroad workers. Their numbers seemed inexhaustible. Colonel William Cody, better known as Buffalo Bill, was one of the hunters, and it has been said that 4,000 animals fell to his rifle alone. Suddenly it was realized that the millions had become a few hundred, and only last-minute action by the Americans saved the bison from extinction. Now the surviving herds live in peace and security in great wildlife reserves.

Africa still has variety of species, many still in large numbers, but these are a remnant of the immense herds of the past.

Nowadays man tries to preserve the remnants—the bison and pronghorn antelope in the U.S.A.; Przewalsky's horse and the saiga antelope of the Asiatic steppes; and a variety of species in the National Parks and Game Reserves of Africa. The saiga now numbers about 2 million head and is an important food animal in the U.S.S.R.

Broomweed replacing sagebrush in New Mexico after man's interference.

The Wombat is an Australian gnawing marsupial, the counterpart of rodents from other parts of the world. It has short legs and strong digging claws. It is nocturnal in habits.

Prairie Dog Town. Prairie Dogs, among the most social of rodents, live together in large family units each with its definite territory in the town. Clan members help each other to dig burrows, share the grazing peaceably and seem to delight in kissing and grooming each other.

Too many mouths

Natural grasslands can support a certain weight and variety of animals that eat grass, and therefore a certain weight and variety of species that prey on them. The weight of grass-eaters it can support without damage to itself is its carrying capacity. Obviously the carrying capacity of any wild grassland is limited, and when too many mouths try to find a living the result is overgrazing.

This happened on a big scale in the U.S.A. where most of the plains grasses are bunch grasses that don't form sod; rather they grow in separate clumps like ferns. The ground in between supports flowering herbs and annual grasses. Too many mouths, aided by too many trampling feet, mean grass rumped down hard and parts of the ground laid bare. This lets in pioneer plants —plants belonging to an earlier stage in the grassland succession—weeds in fact. They cover over the scars until the next stage in the succession. If they keep on spreading it is a sign that overgrazing is continuing. So one of the effects of overgrazing is to set the succession back.

A setback in the succession benefits insects and rodents at the expense of large grazing animals. In North America the prairie dog, the jackrabbit, the kangaroo rat, and the ground squirrels, all increase in numbers on overgrazed range. All are burrowers, and all require short grass to give them a field of view. They cannot flourish on tall grass prairie, and they cannot

turn long grass into short grass. It has to be done for them. Cattle can do it by overgrazing. So a large population of prairie dogs is a result of overgrazing, not a cause of it.

It has, in fact, been clearly shown that broken down range can recover, and proceed to its proper tall grass climax, if large grazing animals are removed for a while, even if rodents like prairie dogs and ground squirrels remain. The rodents by themselves cannot arrest the succession, and may disappear altogether from the range.

Once prairie dogs are present in large numbers they compete with cattle for the grass, and let in weeds by keeping the ground bare round their mounds. Range continues to deteriorate and cattle suffer. So man has taken action against the prairie dogs. He has cut their millions to a few scattered colonies; and the populous dog *towns*, which once covered many square miles and were linked from horizon to horizon, are now things of the past.

The European Rabbit is a grazing animal that has adapted itself to many habitats—the forest fringe, the hillside, high quality pasture and rough grazings. It was brought to England by the Normans and has since colonized the whole of Britain.

Enter the rodents

By killing predators at the same time as he killed grass-eaters man has taken a lot of the pressure off ground squirrels, kangaroo rats and jackrabbits. All have benefited from the destruction of wolves, coyotes, badgers, foxes, hawks, owls and snakes. Man killed the big predators to save lambs, calves and poultry, but the cost of range eaten by rodents and rabbits is almost certainly greater than the value of stock destroyed by predators. The

In North America the Bison is popularly known as the Buffalo. The remnants of the once great herds are now protected in special wildlife reserves.

black-footed ferret, a predator on the prairie dog, has suffered along with its prey, and is now threatened with extinction.

On the world's other grasslands other rodents occupy the niches occupied in America by ground squirrels, prairie dogs, rats and jackrabbits. Africa has its own races of ground squirrels. Australia has the native wombat and the introduced European rabbit. In Eastern Europe there are susliks (ground squirrels), hamsters, and bobaks (marmots of the steppes). South America has the cavy (guinea pig), and the viscacha (chinchilla).

In Eastern Europe the ground squirrels are found on derelict ground, on ridges and railway embankments, and on verges and rough pastures, where they are not disturbed by the plough. They do not occur on well-managed grasslands, but it is likely they would if the ground was bared or beaten down by overgrazing.

Rodent burrows are sometimes used by other species for their own purposes. Rattlesnakes and burrowing owls use the burrows of prairie dogs on the American Plains, and it used to be thought that the three lived together in family harmony. In fact the owls nest in unused burrows, and sometimes kill young prairie dogs. The rattlesnake shelters in burrows, eats the eggs of the owl at times and young prairie dogs at other times. Bird, reptile and mammal use the same burrows, but they use them at different times. They are no more a happy family than the fox and the badger that sometimes share the same burrow system in European forest and woodland.

Natural grasslands can be added to by grassland derived from forest or scrub. Forest and scrub can be changed to grassland by felling or by fire, and maintained as grassland by grazing and periodic burning. Part of the African veld has been created by fire from forest and bush. Much the same happened in the Scottish Highlands, where hill grazings have been derived from pine and oak forest, and are maintained by grazing and fire.

Savannas

Savannas are tropical grasslands with shrubs or trees—the product of alternating rain and drought. Within 10 degrees north and south of the equator there are two rainy seasons, in one of which rainfall may be slight or fail altogether. North and south of these lines there is only one rainy season, with drought for the rest of the year.

There are savannas in South America, Australia and Africa, but those of Africa are the most extensive and have been most closely studied.

South of the Sahara the savannas change progressively from desert to shrubs with grass, then grass with shrubs, then grass with trees, then trees with grass, then forest.

Because of the uncertain rainfall, and the long dry season, savannas have never been as productive for man as temperate grasslands. Their seeming fertility is an illusion.

Cattle-ranching on the plains of the United States of America. Modern cattle have taken the place of the herds of bison of bygone days.

Well-managed vines on a South African farm. Here man has turned former grassland into highly productive agricultural land.

Except in moister parts cultivation has never been successful, as the soil becomes exhausted after a few years. Grazing has also created its own problems.

The sight of grass in plenty has always tempted man to put his cattle and sheep on to eat it, often with disastrous results. Man sees the teeming wildlife thriving on limitless grazings, and at once imagines he can replace them with cattle and sheep. Yet when he does so the range suffers. The range that can support, without damage, enormous wild herds in bewildering variety, deteriorates quickly, even to the point of no return, when these are replaced by much smaller numbers of sheep and cattle. The secret is the variety of mouths, not the number.

The savannas are ancient ecosystems, untouched and uninterrupted by the Ice Ages. Wildlife and habitat have long been finely knit together in a close fabric. The variety of game animals, each in its niche, is in subtle balance with the habitat. Each species is a vital thread in the delicate fabric. Each operates in its own feeding niche, upsetting no other; so the habitat remains productive and continues in being. The wildlife grew up with the habitat, in fact, so the two are in harmony.

Each to his own

This great variety of grazing and browsing animals forms a very broad array, or *spectrum*, and each species moves through the habitat on a narrow, clearly defined front, meeting its special needs from the habitat's special resources. Cattle, sheep, and goats, which are alien to the habitat, form a narrow *spectrum* of three, and operate on all fronts at the same time, taking what they can get. The wild animals move from place to place, so no front is devastated; the vegetation recovers when the mouths depart. Sheep, goats, and cattle are herded and held in one place; so many fronts are punished all the time,

The Leopard is a versatile hunter found on savannas and in forest.

Impala at a waterhole. Large ungulates like the impala have to live within travelling distance of the scattered water-holes at which herds made up of many species can be seen.

and the vegetation naturally suffers.

Agriculture and stock-raising have come up against other ecological realities on savanna. Leslie Brown has shown that it costs 60/– per acre to clear bush for subsistence agriculture—that is to allow a farmer to grow enough to feed himself and his family. Yet the annual return is only 1/– from each acre cleared. And the land becomes exhausted in five or six years.

The role of the tsetse fly

The tsetse fly of African savannas has barred a quarter of the land surface south of the Sahara against domestic livestock. The tsetse sucks the blood of wild mammals and birds, and transmits their blood parasites to man and livestock—except poultry. These parasites cause Sleeping Sickness in human beings and *Ngana* in livestock. Wild, hoofed animals carry the parasites in their blood but do not suffer from the disease.

Stockmen are therefore constantly at war with the tsetse fly, while many ecologists argue that the answer would be to leave the African savannas to the wild animals. They could then be cropped for meat and provide the basis of a tourist industry. Tourism is worth £7 million a year in Kenya, where agriculture is worth £12 million.

By barring certain savanna areas against livestock the tsetse fly has saved some big game species from extinction in parts of Africa.

The tsetse of savanna needs bush to breed in, and man fights it with fire and insecticides; he also kills out the big game whose blood it sucks. Such programmes are based on the assumption that what man wants to do with savanna is better than nature's way. The assumption is open to question. The means of destroying the fly are available, but costly. The ecological cost, which is less easy to work out, could be even greater, apart altogether from the loss of wildlife.

All too often, by ignoring ecological factors, man achieves the opposite of what he sets out to do. In one part of Africa, where impala antelope were numerous and warthogs few, the tsetse flies preferred to suck the blood of warthogs—the rate of preference being twenty sucks of warthog blood to one suck of anything else, including impala. The warthog was therefore a prime target for shooting.

But burning of bush at the same time favoured a grass much liked by warthogs, whose food supply increased. So, despite heavy shooting, warthogs became more numerous than before, while the tsetse fly was not reduced. The end result was a bigger reservoir of infected blood for tsetse flies to suck.

There are relationships on savannas more complicated than that. One such close-knit ecological web has termites as a main strand:

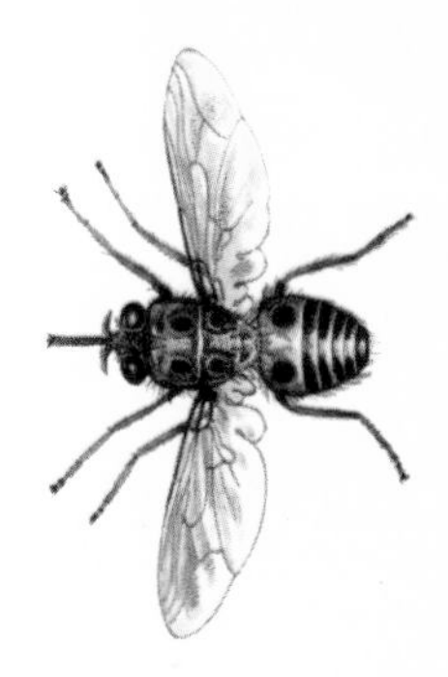

CYNODON GRASS ←——— IMPALA ←——————— LEOPARD
↑ ↓
TERMITES ———→ ACACIA TORTILIS ←——— GIRAFFE
↑
AARDVARK ——————→ MELON

Termites' niche, on acacia savanna in Tanzania (based on East African Journal of Wildlife, after Lamprey).

The Tsetse fly, which is no bigger than a house-fly, has barred many parts of Africa to man and his livestock.

Acacia tortilis is a thorny tree whose dead wood is eaten by termites. Abandoned termite mounds, broken down and scattered, make a seed bed for Cynodon Grass, which is the food of the impala in the dry season. At other seasons the impala eats acacia pods, and passes the seeds with its droppings. The action of the impala's digestive system weakens the tough skins of the seeds and helps their germination. The leaves of the new acacias are eaten by giraffes and the cycle of dead wood to termites begins again. The aardvark preys on termites. It also eats a species of water melon for the water content, and then helps the melons to grow by burying its dung with their seeds wrapped up in it. The leopard preys upon impala.

The Warthog is an important animal on African savannas because it is a common victim of tsetse-fly attack and therefore a host for the parasite of Sleeping Sickness. Many attempts have been made to reduce the tsetse-fly by killing off host species like the warthog but most of these have ended in failure.

Elephants at a waterhole in Kruger National Park, South Africa. In Africa the elephant has played a major role in changing savanna country into grassland. The idea that the African elephant cannot be domesticated is erroneous. Hannibal used them when he crossed the Alps.

Fire—master and servant

Throughout African savannas the delicate balance between grass and trees is maintained by fire—natural and man-made. The trees are deciduous and shed their leaves at the beginning of the drought. Dry leaves and dry grass are an annual fire hazard.

When fire runs through a grassy area it kills seedling trees, scorches mature trees and burns shrubs down to the rootstock. At the next rain the grass spreads its cover. If fires do not occur the trees steal ground from the grass, but because of the dry climate they cannot make close forest and exclude the grass altogether.

Man makes most of the fires. He burns to clear ground for cultivation or to make travel easier. He burns off withered grass before the rains, so that there will be quick growth when they come. The young growth attracts game he wants to catch. He burns to drive game out of cover and he burns to destroy ticks and other parasites.

All this burning can cause some soil erosion, but its effect varies from place to place. Fire has been used in such ways by man since time immemorial, but is generally disapproved of nowadays as a tool in land management, although controlled fire still has its uses. It has been truly said that "fire is a good servant and a bad master".

It has proved a bad master in Barotseland where the teak is a valuable timber tree, susceptible to fire, and where fires have increased in number and destructiveness as big game animals have been killed out.

Big game

When big game animals gather near waterholes in the dry season they eat down the inflammable grass, thus reducing the fire risk to the teaks growing there. By keeping the bush understory open they make room for young teaks to grow up. Beetles carry the animals' dung below the surface and hoofs tread the seed into the rich mixture. So the teak flourishes where there is big game.

When the big game is killed out for one reason or another the dry grass is consumed by fires which also destroy teak seedlings and adult trees. The trees are gradually replaced by fire-resistant bush which grows thick from the ground up as there are no animals to open the understory. In such conditions teak seedlings cannot grow.

Fire and elephants together can turn savanna into grassland. Too many elephants damage the trees and bush and let in grass. The grass lets in fire to destroy more trees and bush, whose destruction lets in still more grass. In twenty to thirty years the savanna becomes grassland.

Man can turn forest into savanna by fire, axe, and grazing by livestock. This is derived savanna. The burning or the felling lets in grass, which is eaten by grazing animals. The trees are held back by the joint action of burning and grazing, and the area kept as savanna.

Savannas are much drier than forests, and the destruction of forests is making Africa drier year by year.

The rains come

The rainy season on savannas anywhere is the creative time, the time of growth for vegetation and breeding for many birds. The weaver birds of Africa start nesting, using the new green shoots for building. The males don their brilliant plumage, an event described by the Hausa tribe of Nigeria as the king putting on his robes. The young weavers are growing when the savanna grasses are seeding to provide them with food. If the rain does not last the weavers desert their nests. If the rain is late nesting is late. If the rain doesn't come the birds emigrate to look for it elsewhere.

Desert locusts breed during the rainy season when there is green food for their larvae. In East Africa, where there are two rainy seasons, they breed twice. Where there is one rainy season they breed once. In the few places that have three rains the locusts breed three times.

The red-capped dotterel of Australia is found on dry savanna as well as on the coast of Victoria. On the savanna it nests beside temporary lagoons formed by cloudbursts. Cloudbursts come at any season, so the dotterel breeds at any season. On the dry savannas of Australia and Africa rainfall also affects the number of eggs laid by birds. They lay bigger clutches in wet years than in dry ones, presumably because food is more plentiful in wet years.

But not all bird species breed when the rains come. Many birds of prey breed in the dry season, perhaps because their prey species bred in the wet season and are most numerous following it. The prey is more easily seen then because the cover is poorer.

The small dik-dik antelope of Tanzania has two breeding times—one at the beginning and one at the end of the rainy season. In the first the young start life in the cool season of long grass; in the second they start off in the hot season when grass is shorter. But in both cases the young dik-diks are born in the shelter of long grass. Cover, not rain, is what matters here.

Locusts set out on their long migrations when their numbers on their home ground become so great that the insects are virtually rubbing shoulders with each other. So long as they have plenty of room they do not migrate. Migration is therefore a phase that occurs only when the number of locusts has reached a certain level. At other times, locusts are stay-at-homes.

CANOPY

CHAPTER 6

THE FORESTS

The forests of the world fall naturally into three main types—coniferous forests; deciduous forests (also called hardwood or broad-leaved); and rain forests.

The coniferous forest belt girdles the world south of the tundra. Deciduous forests grow in the north temperate zone, which is warmer and moister. Rain forests of broad-leaved evergreens are found in the tropics of South America, West Africa, India, Malaysia, and North-east Australia. In tropical regions that have a dry season the trees are usually deciduous, and grow in open formation known as woodland or savanna woodland.

Each belt has its dominant climax trees. The coniferous belt of North America has mainly spruce, fir and larch, with some pines. The north temperate zone has oak with beech, or oak with hickory and long-leaved pines. The Mediterranean slopes of the Alps have beech and fir. Temperate California has giant redwoods and sitka spruce. Tropical rain forest has immense variety, up to 300 species to the square mile.

There is also zoning by height above sea level. On Mount Kenya there is rain forest up to 6000 feet; then bamboo for another 1000 feet; then grassland. On the Adriatic Coast of Europe the low ground is

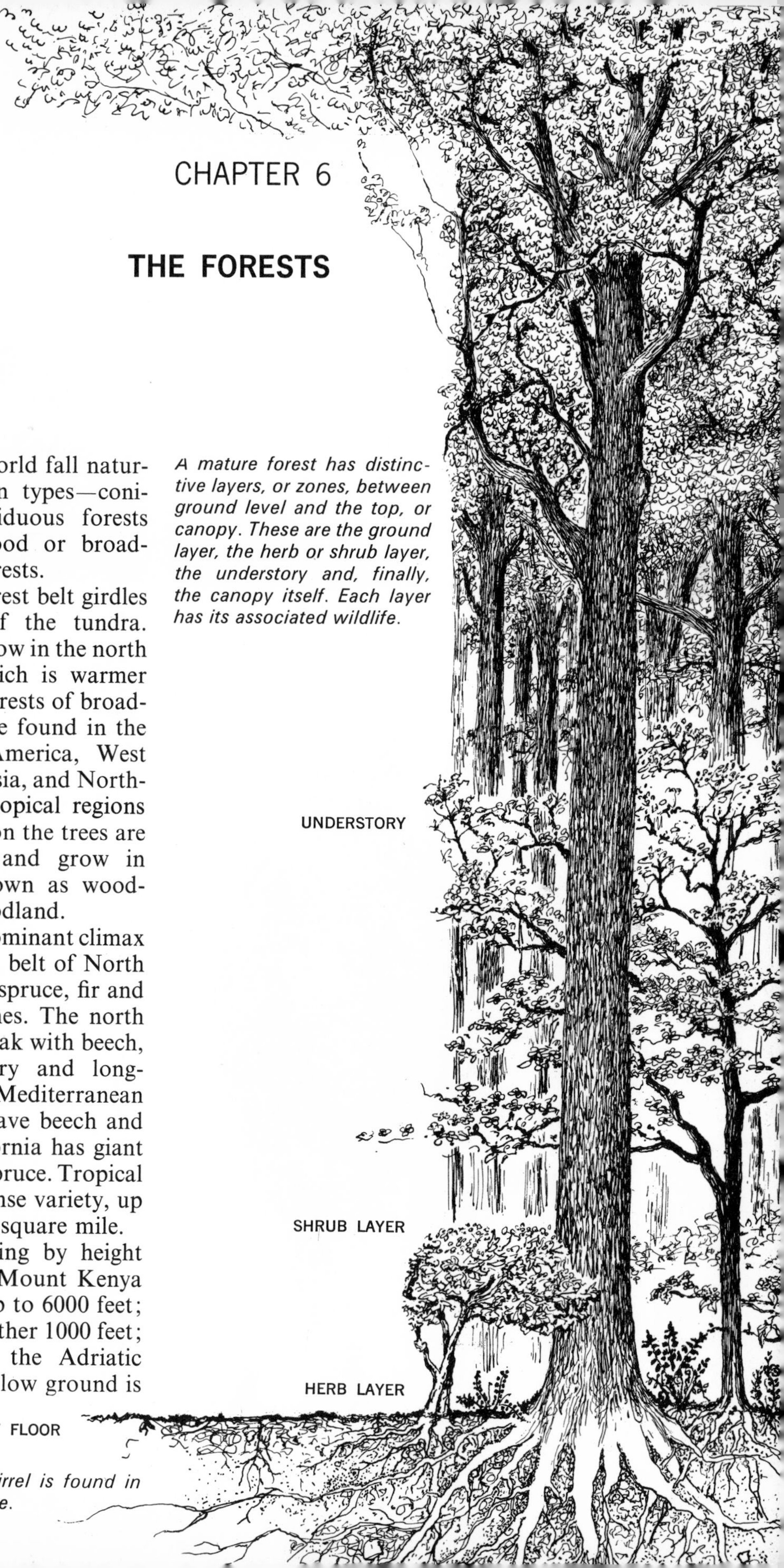

A mature forest has distinctive layers, or zones, between ground level and the top, or canopy. These are the ground layer, the herb or shrub layer, the understory and, finally, the canopy itself. Each layer has its associated wildlife.

UNDERSTORY

SHRUB LAYER

HERB LAYER

FOREST FLOOR

The European Red Squirrel is found in forests of pine and spruce.

Each zone of altitude on a mountain slope has different vegetation according to conditions of temperature, moisture, exposure and soil. Diagram shows the zones on a mountain in Rocky Mountain National Park, Colorado.

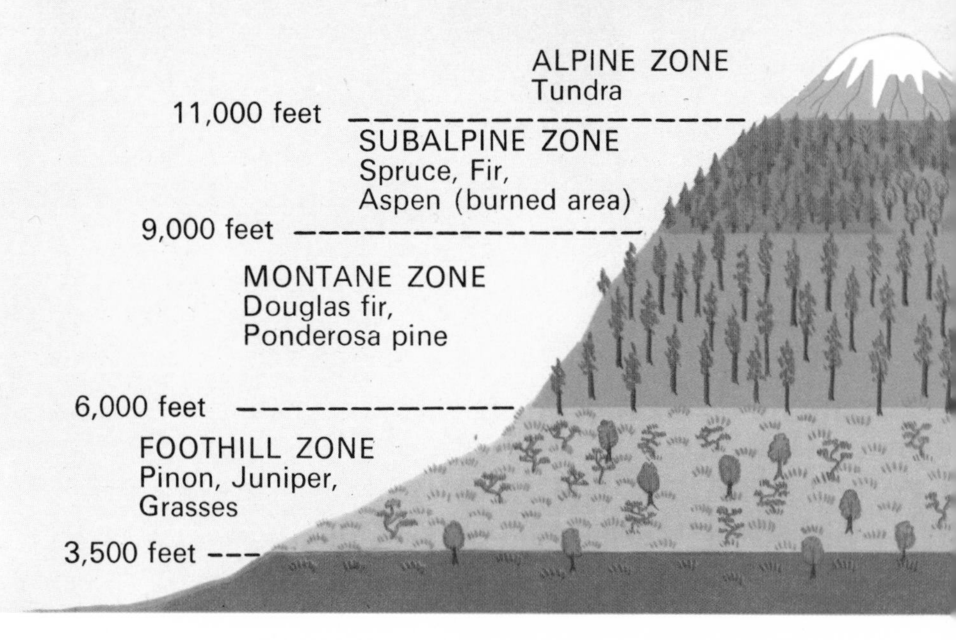

The Elk is the biggest deer in the world. In the U.S.A. it is known as the Moose.

maquis scrub, rising to beech and fir, rising to montane pine, and then treeless grassland.

Looked at from the ground up, forests will be seen to have several levels, or layers, of vegetation—the ground layer or herbage floor; the shrub layer; the small tree layer; and the climax layer, or canopy. Dense coniferous forest, with a floor of dead needles, has no layers between ground and crown. Once it is opened up, so that light gets in, it will produce a ground layer, and perhaps a shrub layer. Deciduous forest has several layers. Rain forest has most.

The Borealis Race

The most northerly zone of the coniferous belt is the Boreal Forest (from Boreas, god of the North Wind), which is mainly of sombre spruce and fir—a forest of spires with flexible drooping branches, fit to bear and quick to shed their weight of snow. Southwards the boreal forest merges into community with larch, hemlock, pine and cedar, and with hardwoods like alder, willow and birch.

During the past million years the boreal region has been several times under ice, so the landscape has been worn to a monotonous level, now covered by dark spruce forest. The permafrost means the trees have shallow roots and are easily blown down by high winds. Because of the poor drainage the region is fretted with lakes and marshes—the muskegs.

Fire and storm tear great wounds in the forest—gaps where the succession can begin again. When the trees are blown or burned on low ground it floods to become muskeg. The succession from muskeg begins with a cover of sphagnum, followed by grass and sedge, then berry shrubs, then birch, willow and alder, and on to climax. So the forest's face has many scars—each a stage in the succession.

These seral stages, as they are called, have their own animal associates. The moose haunts the swamps, browsing twigs and leafage, and eating the water plants, but lies up in the timber. White-tailed deer of North America browse shrubs and young hardwoods, but shelter in the forest. Shelter is as important to them as food in winter, and when they herd in the forest during the worst of the snow they may die of hunger in comfort, or kill off seedling trees by browsing.

Birds of the forest

In the North American spruce forests two out of three birds are warblers. In Europe and Asia the warblers are fewer in numbers and species, and the species are different. The grouse of European forests is the capercaillie, a giant weighing 11 pounds or more. Its relative in North America is the blue grouse, which weighs less than $3\frac{1}{2}$ pounds. Another American is the spruce grouse weighing only $1\frac{1}{4}$ pounds. These match the black grouse of Europe, which are birds of the forest edge.

Birds spread up as well as out into their special niches. In mixed forest of Alpine Fir and Engelmann Spruce the highest level is occupied by siskins, pine grosbeaks and goldcrests; lower down are tree creepers and warblers; lower still another species of goldcrest. The ground beneath the trees is the niche of the American robin. Tits and goldcrests sort themselves out in the same way on Scots Pine in England—the goldcrests at the top; the coal tit and blue tit lower down;

The White-tailed Deer of North America is the ecological equivalent of the Roe Deer in Europe and occupies the same sort of niche in forest and scrub.

The Long-eared Owl of Europe is a bird of dark, coniferous forest and is strictly nocturnal in habits.

the willow tit and the long-tailed tit lower still; and the great tit lowest of all, below 12 feet.

Four-fifths of the forest birds are migrants, arriving with the spring and leaving in the autumn to spend the winter farther south. Birds like the grosbeaks can stay all the time, but will move out in years of poor seed harvest.

Harvesters and planters

The red squirrel is a common animal of the mature forest, and feeds mainly on cone seeds. When gathering the cones of the black spruce the red squirrel nips off the twigs below the crown, baring the stem for some way down. This leaves the tree with a tuft on top. The bared stem acts as a barrier to the flames during a forest fire; the lower foliage is burned off but the tuft escapes. The cones of the tuft survive to shed seeds to grow new trees in the ashes of the old.

Outside their niche of cone-bearing forest, red squirrels are colonizers, squatters you might say. They can do well in other niches so long as the rightful occupants are not there. In deciduous forest the grey squirrel holds the niche and can keep the red squirrel out. The fox squirrel of North America also has its special niche, which it can hold against the grey.

Squirrels, in fact, are worth looking at as niche holders. In the days when America had almost unlimited hardwood forests the grey squirrel was an abundant animal. Its niche was mature forest of oak and

Cock Capercaillie displaying in spring in Northern European spruce forest. The capercaillie is the biggest grouse in the world. For a great part of the year it feeds mainly on the leading shoots and buds of coniferous trees.

The Red Squirrel of Canada is found in pine or spruce forest, mixed hardwood forest and swamp forest.

First stage succession after the felling of a forest in North America. Golden rods and asters are the main plants in this initial battle of succession, but in the fifth or sixth year changes begin to take place. Small trees and shrubs begin to appear. When the golden rods and asters die down to their roots each autumn, the young trees remain standing and have a head start in the spring. Gradually they shade out the competitors.

hickory. The forest edge, the fringe, was the niche of the fox squirrel. The American pioneers cut the habitat of the grey squirrel to pieces when they felled the hardwood forests, so it suffered a decline. The bits and pieces left suited fox squirrels, which continued to prosper. The grey could not take the pieces from them any more than it had been able to take the fringe from them before the felling.

When the grey was introduced to England, where it is not a native, it settled in at once in small woods and spinneys, the very niches it could not hold in its native America. But, in England, there were no fox squirrels to keep it out.

There were, however, red squirrels. But red squirrels are really inhabitants of coniferous forests. For them, small woods and spinneys are secondary niches. The grey squirrel proved better able to fill them, and in this situation came out on top. It has done much the same in Scotland, where its spread has been halted by the coniferous barrier, inside which the red squirrel rules in strength. It may yet be able to make something even out of this situation but that remains to be seen.

Renewal and replacement

Deciduous forests have been exten-

sively cleared by man because he wanted the ground for farming. Vast areas of America were cleared of their hardwood heritage in this way. Over much of Europe such forests exist now only as preserved remnants, as in Poland and Bohemia. In Britain hardwoods make up no more than small woodlands, spinneys, copses and coppices, rich in plant and animal life. France has large hardwood forests, planted and maintained by man.

A deciduous forest cleared of trees would grow back to deciduous forest if succession was allowed to begin and go on to the end. Man, by farming, prevents it beginning. If it begins he can stop it at any point he likes.

In Britain, ground cleared of hardwoods is taken over first of all by pioneering plants like foxglove, fireweed, dock and thistle. This is followed by second growth of trees like birch, rowan and hazel, with foxgloves and other plants still part of the community. Then the conifers appear, and grow on, cutting off the light from their competitors. But hardwood seedlings can stand shade, so they grow up and in the end replace the conifers. The climax is hardwoods again, or hardwoods with groups of conifers.

Ground cleared of hardwoods is often replanted with conifers to supply a quick crop; but planting with a single species of conifer brings its own troubles—disease being one. When disease takes hold it can run through the whole forest because all the trees are alike, and there is nothing to prevent it spreading from one to another. Mixed planting erects barriers by bringing in variety.

The Germans used to plant one kind of tree over a large area, growing the type most in demand at the time. They gave this up a long time ago, and now go in for mixed planting and selective felling, which are more like nature's way. The old way was to clear fell the forest then replant. Selective felling means felling strips here and there, year by year, and replanting them as they are cleared, so that the forest has trees of all ages.

With hardwoods, individual trees are felled, and seedlings planted in the area formerly covered by the canopy. The Germans put up nesting boxes for tits and other insect-eating birds, because they have found that the trees do better when the birds are encouraged than when they are not present.

American foresters have been slow to learn from the German experience, and mixed planting is still not widely practised. In Australia the native eucalyptus trees are still being replaced almost entirely by Monterey Pines from North

Blue Tit at nesting box in woodland. Tits are encouraged in this way in German forests.

The Great Spotted Woodpecker bores its nesting hole in dying trees or trees already dead.

The European Sparrowhawk feeds mainly on small birds which it surprises on or near the ground. It nests in woodland usually at a considerable height and prefers larches to nest in.

America. Nature's way, which is variety, is the best way but man still finds it convenient to plant forests of one species, despite the risks. Mixed planting is still not widely practised, and slow-growing hardwoods are usually left out altogether.

France plants hardwoods on a big scale, especially oak and beech. The British Forestry Commission, once dedicated to growing conifers, which mature quickly, is beginning to plant hardwoods, which grow slowly. In Britain there is some planting of hardwoods for amenity, and as cover for game birds. The vanished oak woods of Scotland cannot regenerate because the hillsides they grew on are now permanently grazed by sheep and deer.

The forest wildlife

Natural forests or woodlands—with uprooted trees, logs, stumps, plants and secondary growth—look untidy compared with the commercial forester's regimented dream plantations. But they are all the better for that. They provide niches for a much greater variety of plants and animals.

Bears like cut-over forest where they can find plenty of berry bushes, and roots, and tubers, and rotting stumps with insects and larvae. The wild boar of Europe eats the fruits of trees like oak, chestnut and beech,

and prepares the ground for their seedlings when digging with its nose for tubers. At the same time it turns up and eats mice which eat the seeds. Squirrels bury nuts and trees grow from the ones they forget about. The jay, a crow, helps oak woods to spread uphill by burying acorns which are too heavy to be blown there by the wind.

Individual trees provide niches for a variety of animal life, especially insects. The oak is one. From its crown to its roots it is truly a house of many mansions.

Caterpillars of the winter moth and the leaf roller feed on the oak's foliage, and are in turn eaten by tits, jackdaws, rooks, and starlings. Gall

European Roebuck with antlers in the velvet in February. A mature roebuck stands under $2\frac{1}{2}$ feet tall at the shoulder and weighs usually under 60 pounds. The roe deer is foxy-red in colour in summer, much greyer in winter.

European Badgers emerging from their sett at nightfall. Badgers are nocturnal.

The Woodpigeon is a large, tree-nesting dove. It breeds several times each year.

wasps cause the growths known as oak apples and marble galls. On the leaves are spangle galls and current galls. There are even galls on the roots. Jays eat acorns. The acorn itself is a whole ecosystem, bored, invaded, eaten and slept in by a variety of insect and other parasites. When healthy acorns fall to the ground they are eaten by pheasants, woodpigeons, mice, squirrels and badgers; when the diseased ones fall their parasites emerge and their place is taken by the breakdown gangs in the breaker's yard of the soil.

Rain forests

The richest of all forest ecosystems in variety of plant and animal life is tropical rain forest. A square mile of rain forest will have from 200 to 300 species of large trees and an equal variety of smaller ones, all of them broad-leaved but evergreen like pines. Lianas climb, twist, and trail over the trees, and hang from them like drapes. Orchids and ferns grow in profuse variety. Familiar plants of temperate regions—violets, roses and ferns—become large and woody, even tree-like, in the rain forest.

The forest is hot and humid, the temperature not rising nor falling. The shade is deep and almost permanent. On the ground the green growth is scant except where a big tree falls and lets in light. Then there is a rush of green, but such glades are quickly shaded out again by the quick growth of a new tree. Some plants, like the spiny bush grape, can stand the gloom, and even have colourful flowers to attract pollinating insects.

The eye cannot see far in rain forest despite the scant ground vegetation. Lianas, ferns and rotting trunks obstruct the view. Upwards the eye can follow the columns of the large trees only as far as the first canopy; then they are lost. The layers above are a secret world, teeming with life to the very roof of the forest, and to the crowns of the tallest trees that project above it. The life at these high levels can barely be glimpsed from the ground.

In the hot, humid atmosphere the breakdown of ground litter is fast. Termites, bacteria and fungi work at speed on dead leaves, twigs, rotting trees, and the dead bodies of animals, so the amount of leaf mould present at any time is less than in temperate deciduous forest. The fertility added to the earth by dead trees is taken back again quickly by the living.

There is great variety of animal species, although the variety is not always matched by number of indi-

The hen Capercaillie nests on the ground, usually near the base of a tree.

The Canada Lynx is a specialist predator on the Snowshoe Hare.

viduals of the species. You might see 130 species of birds in a single day, without seeing many individuals of any one of them.

On the ground are toads, lizards, ant-eaters and armadillos: all insect-eaters. The armadillo is the only mammal, apart from the hedgehog, that can roll itself into a complete ball. Browsing animals are not numerous. South American rain forest has the tapir and a few species of deer. In Africa there are elephant, buffalo, okapi, bongo, bushbuck, and forest hogs. The elephant and buffalo of the forests are smaller than their kin of the savannas. The okapi and the bongo are solitary animals; so are antelopes like bushbuck and duiker. Predators include the jaguar, leopard, tiger and a variety of weasels.

Small antelopes are difficult to see in the rain forest, but the forest eagle catches them. It sits high, on a look-out tree, and swoops when it sees one. It also catches monkeys.

Holding hands and twining tails

A very large number of species is specially adapted for living in trees. Some make use of their tail for holding on with, so that it becomes an extra limb. A monkey that can hang by its tail is using it as a fifth hand. The spider, howler and woolly monkeys of South America use their tails in this way. Such tails are prehensile. The Old World monkeys, and the squirrel monkeys of the New World, do not have such tails.

Monkeys are not the only animals with prehensile tails. The pangolins of Africa and Java have them. The tree mice of Papua and the tree porcupines of South America have them. So have the collared ant-eater, the two-toed ant-eater, and the kinkajou. Some African flying squirrels have another device—spines on the underside of the tail which act as an anti-skid tread when the animals are climbing trees with smooth bark.

Feet that can be used like hands

Rain forest occurs in South America, Africa, Indo-Malaysia, and Australia, wherever sunlight, moisture and warmth are abundant throughout the year. Rain forests are stable habitats that have been little disturbed by changes in climate for several millions of years. As a result they have had time to evolve an immense variety of plant and animal life.

The Porcupine of North America is a forest animal that lives in trees and feeds on bark. When on the ground it defends itself against enemies with its tail, the quills of which loosen when they penetrate the enemies' skin.

are a help in climbing, because the toes can close like fingers and take a grip. Monkeys are hand-footed; men are not. But man has skilful hands. He can touch the tip of his fingers with the tip of the thumb, which is another way of saying that he can oppose his thumb to all his other fingers. This permits him to hold and handle objects with great precision. Some rain forest animals have developed similar abilities.

The Brazilian tree rat can oppose the first two toes of its foot to the other three, so it is able to climb up smooth bamboo. The Malayan tree rat can oppose its first finger but not its thumb. The long-tailed tree mouse of India and Indo China has the first and fifth fingers of the hands and feet opposed. The South American tree porcupine and the two-toed ant-eater can oppose the four toes of the fore-foot against the sole of the hindfoot which has an anti-skid device.

Some animals have developed toes with suckers for giving them a hold, examples being the frogs, the tarsiers of Indo-Malaysia, and the sucker-footed bats of Madagascar. Others, like lizards, frogs, and some marsupial mammals, have a skin fold between fore and hind legs which acts as a parachute, enabling them to glide from tree to tree.

Many rain forest frogs are permanent tree dwellers, and have well developed suckers for holding on. Some of these frogs glue leaves together to make envelopes in which they lay their eggs. Others simply glue their eggs to leaves. Yet others carry the eggs on their backs, and their tadpoles complete their growth inside the sacs.

The forest spreads its influence

Every forest is an ecosystem with its own community of trees, and its niches for plants and animals, all related to each other in some subtle or obvious way. But any forest is something more than the sum of its trees, just as any tree is something more than a unit of forest. A forest is more than its trees, more than its plants, more than its niches, more than its wildlife, more than an ecological community, more than an

Deciduous forest occurs on good soil in a cool, moist climate. Deciduous forest is a patchwork of colour in autumn just before leaf-fall when the leaves of each kind of tree change to different shades of red, orange and yellow.

ecosystem. It spreads its influence far beyond its boundaries.

On watersheds it holds water—in the body and leaves of its trees and like a sponge at their roots. It therefore controls the run-off and drainage of water to the lower slopes and the valleys. If the tree cover is removed from the watershed all the rain that falls drains or runs away, swelling the mountain streams, then the rivers, and causing floods on the low ground and in the valleys. The soil itself is washed or blown away from the watershed, leaving it bare, so that trees cannot be replanted. The soil washed down silts up rivers and estuaries, and debris is deposited on arable ground and pasture.

Forests on steep hillsides hold the soil, and control the run of water. If they are clear felled, and not quickly replanted, the soil is washed down to choke the streams. If the erosion is not halted by replanting the hillside becomes completely bared to the rock so that trees cannot grow at all.

Forests along a river give shelter and prevent extremes of temperature, thus benefiting fish. Drainage and run-off are controlled as on the watershed, which means control of soil erosion, which means less silt and debris deposited in the river. The forest also provides shelter for animals, including domestic stock grazing the bottom land.

Many of the problems of modern land use have their roots where the roots of vanished forests were once in complete control.

When a hillside or ravine is felled of its tree cover, the ground is exposed to the action of wind, rain, snow and ice and the topsoil will erode into the valley below unless new trees are planted quickly after the standing forest has been felled.

The European Wild Pig, or Wild Boar, is a forest animal. Although mainly a vegetarian it will also eat woodmice which it unearths during its rooting in the soil. The boar is hunted as a trophy animal in many parts of Europe.

CHAPTER 7

INLAND WATERS

The life blood of land is water, which falls as rain to be taken up by plants, without which no other life can survive. But rain also drains or runs away to become springs, streams, rivers, lakes, ponds and marshes, which are ecosystems in their own right.

A river is like a great vein, fed from the watersheds by a network of finer veins, and carrying the life blood of the land to the sea, whence it evaporates into clouds that begin the circulation all over again. Up among the clouds the mountain waters gather from seep and trickle, to feed brooks and streams that leap and spill and froth their way to join the river in the valley below.

The river, swollen by its tributaries, needs elbow room, and makes it by eroding its bed and banks. Its depth and width depend on how it does this. It makes flood plains when it overflows its banks, leaving a deposit of silt. When it deposits a great bulk of silt at its mouth it makes a delta, like the Nile, the Rhône and the Mississippi.

Where ice has gouged out hollows, or where the land has sunk as in the Rift Valley of Africa, the river leaves water behind as lakes. The biggest lakes, hundreds of miles long, are like inland seas. The smallest are hardly bigger than ponds.

Swamps are really lakes where the water is shallow enough to let vegetation grow all over them. Marshes are low-lying wet land, wetter in winter than in summer. Coastal marshes are salt, bathed by the sea. Swamp can become marsh when plants like reeds encroach, growing and rotting down, forming a mat that collects silt and debris.

A pond is a small area of water, stagnant and shallow, with rooted plants growing all over the bottom. There is hardly any movement of the water, and temperature can vary widely from surface to bottom. There are many kinds of ponds, but it is easier to recognize one than to define one.

Animals that live in water face two main problems—getting enough oxygen, and staying in one place, holding on in fact.

The air ways

The oxygen content of water varies. The broken water of a river traps oxygen from the air, so is rich in it. A still pond traps hardly any, and depends on its green plants for its supply. They release it during photosynthesis which, of course, stops when the sun goes down. So the supply in pond water at night is low. The water of a dark, evil-smelling pond has hardly any oxygen at all. The clear cold water flowing over salmon spawning redds is full of it.

The Canada Goose likes islands on freshwater lakes in the nesting season.

The Common Frog hibernates from late autumn until spring then makes its way to its traditional pond for spawning.

Aquatic insects have evolved many ways of breathing. The Donacia *larva, gets oxygen by burrowing into air-filled roots of water lilies and other plants. The water scorpion obtains surface air through a tube formed by two tail filaments edged with interlocking bristles. Many mayfly nymphs have rows of flattened, platelike tracheal gills. The diving beetle carries an air bubble beneath its wing covers.*

There are more ways of getting air in water than of getting water in the desert.

Fish extract oxygen directly from the water as it passes over their gills. Frogs breathe through their mouths and skins on land and through their skins in the water; their tadpoles have gills. Reptiles, including crocodiles, have to surface to breathe. So have mammals—the otter, the mink, the muskrat, the beaver, the seal, the water vole and the water shrew.

Water beetles spend most of their lives in the water of ponds. They can fly, and often do, but they do not have to leave the water to breathe. They hang head down below the surface, with their rear end above it, and take air under their wings through a tube. This lasts them for some time underwater. Their larvae have also to surface to breathe.

Some freshwater snails have a gill and can breathe under the water. Others have a lung, which they fill by surfacing. The first type lives mainly in clear water with plenty of oxygen; the second type lives mainly in ponds, where there is less. When the second type lives in clear water with plenty of oxygen it can remain under for much longer periods, breathing through its tissues to supplement the store of air in its lung. A pond snail, with its lung well filled, becomes buoyant and can float quickly to the surface when it releases its hold. It can sink just as quickly by expelling air and withdrawing into its shell.

Mosquito larvae have breathing tubes which they push from just under the surface, a practice that lays the malarial mosquito open to attack by oil sprays on the water. The rat-tailed maggot, which lives

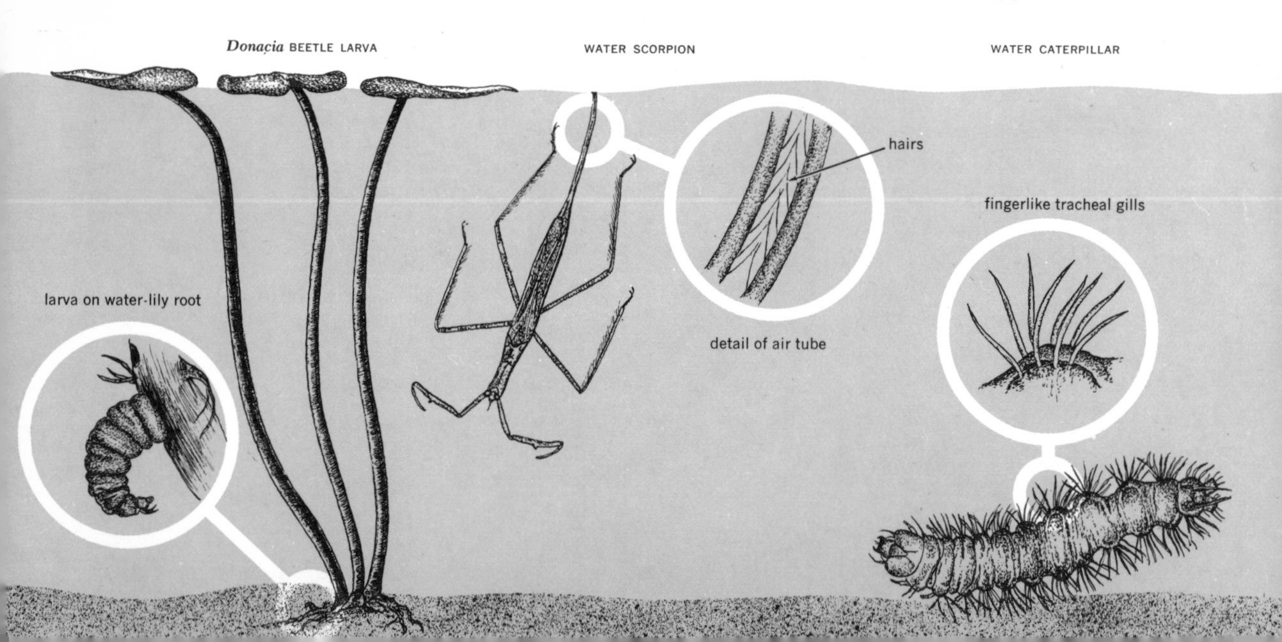

in the black mud of shallow ponds, stays on the bottom and uses its long tail as a breathing tube. The tail is telescopic, and can be lengthened or shortened according to the depth of water in which the maggot is lying.

Other water animals tap the oxygen supply in the stems of plants. Yet others have unwettable hairs in which they trap oxygen, a supply that can be added to slightly from the oxygen in the water. Most of the simpler creatures absorb it through their tissues.

The water spider comes up for air, which it traps in its hair, and this can keep it going for some time; but when it wants to stay under water for long periods, maybe for months on end, it uses a diving bell. The spider weaves a platform of silk which it anchors to water plants. Then it brings down air bubbles, clasped against its body, and releases them underneath its web. The web is pushed up in the middle by the buoyancy of the bubbles and presently a bell is formed.

Inside this bell the spider is independent of the upper air. She seals off a portion of it, and in this separate compartment her young are born. For hibernation, the spider makes another bell later in the year, and at a greater depth.

The Water Vole is a burrowing animal found by ponds and streams. It is an excellent swimmer and diver. It feeds on waterside vegetation.

Ways of holding on

The problem of staying in place, holding on, faces all animals and plants that live in water, and is greatest where the flow is fastest. In still ponds the vegetation can sit up, and animals have no trouble keeping their place. This is also true of quiet backwaters, except during a flood, when plants and animals may be washed away. Wherever water

The Water Spider carries air below the surface to make its air bell.

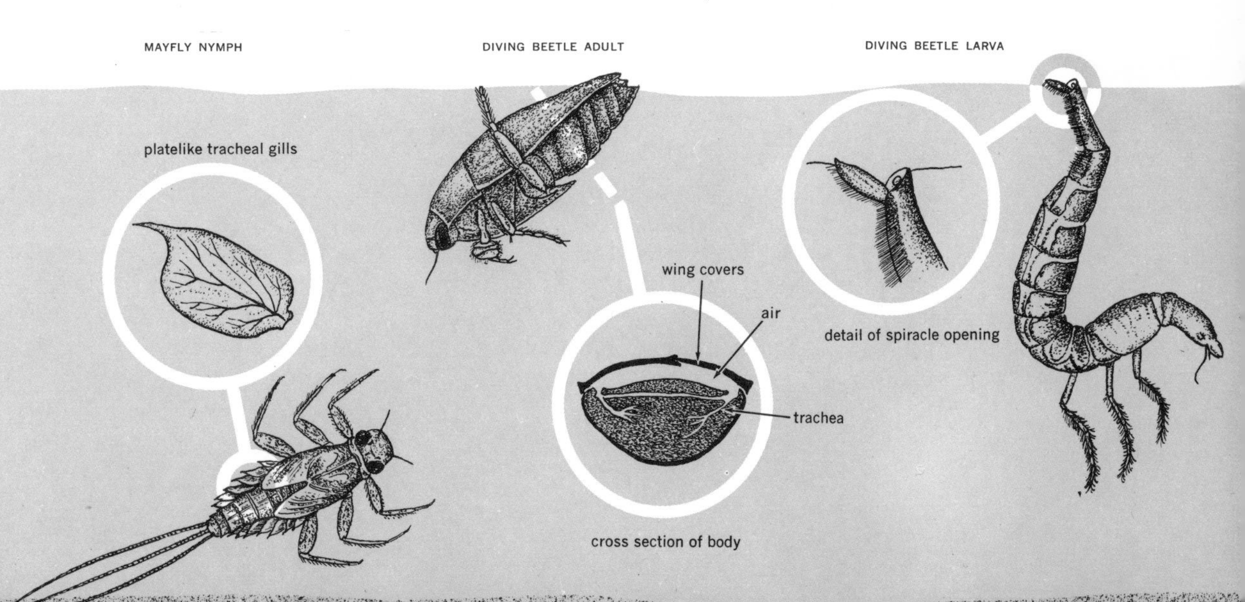

The larvae of the Caddis Fly construct sheltering tubes of vegetation, sand or small pebbles, sometimes including the shells of other small aquatic creatures. The larvae can crawl around with only their fore-end protruding from the tube.

forms waves, as on the shore of a lake, or runs quickly downhill from pool to pool, plants and animals need a good grip.

It is difficult for plants to grow in fast water at all, especially where there is a pebbly or gravelly bottom giving little root hold. Where they do grow, they are of dwarf habit, or cling to rocks and stones, just as trees and shrubs in windy places duck and grow prostrate.

Small animal life responds in several ways. The nymphs of the mayflies have flat bodies; they also have clawed feet to help them crawl over stones in fast flowing water. Caddis fly larvae in fast rivers and streams anchor themselves. Some weave a silken net between stones, with its open end facing upstream. This serves a double purpose. It gives the larva an anchor and catches prey washed downstream.

Other river species sheathe themselves in tubes, like their relatives in ponds. But the pond caddis usually make tubes of lightweight plant material which they can drag around. The river species make their tubes of heavier material, such as sand or gravel, or they attach the tubes to stones.

A common way of staying in place is not to hold on at all, but to hide under heavy stones. The freshwater shrimp and the larvae of the crane-fly do it. So, of course, do fishes like trout and minnows.

When water dries up it can mean the death of many species, but some are able to withstand such droughts. The water flea lays eggs which are resistant to drought, heat and cold —a great boon to a species dependent on water at other stages of its life cycle. Many kinds of drought-resistant mosquitoes lay their eggs in damp hollows, and the eggs do not begin development until rain fills the hollows.

The fairy shrimp breeds in temporary pools and nowhere else. It survives the dry season in the Middle East, and its eggs do not hatch until the pools fill up. This gives it an advantage over animals that can only colonize such pools from a base of permanent water. The lung fishes of Australia, Africa and South America burrow into the mud in the dry season and aestivate —staying just alive and no more.

Minerals and production

Inland waters—rivers, lakes, streams, marshes and ponds—make up only a very small part of the earth's surface, but they are an important one. The productivity of the best lakes, marshes and rivers is greater than that of grasslands, or even agricultural land.

Minerals are as vital to the life of lakes as they are to life on land. They arrive in solution or suspension and nourish plants, rooted or floating, which feed animals, which feed other animals. So the whole life of the lake really depends on the geology of the country from which it draws its water. Poor rocks mean few nutrients washed down. If the drainage is rich the lake is enriched.

Some water food chains are short; others, more complicated, are really food webs. But short or complicated, minerals are locked up in them until the plants and animals die. Then the minerals are freed for re-use by plants. How they are kept in circulation depends a lot on climate and depth of water.

Minerals that sink to the bottom in deep water may be lost because plants cannot grow at the depth to bring them up again. This is what happens in some of the deep lakes in the Rift Valley of Africa.

In shallower lakes wind helps to keep the water stirred from top to

The Heron fishes in ponds, rivers, lakes and in sheltered bays and estuaries. It is an expert fisherman. Besides fish it eats frogs, mice and beetles. Herons nest early in the year, using tall trees, often at some distance from the water.

bottom, so the minerals remain in circulation. Circulation is further helped by the behaviour of the water itself. In the northern winter the water is colder on the top than on the bottom, and becomes warmer towards the bottom. These layers of different temperature are the Temperature Gradient. The cold water on the surface sinks, and the warmer water below rises to take its place. This cools and sinks again, and again, and the constant ups and downs keep nutrients circulating.

Food chains

In fresh water, the first line animals feed on the rich pastures of plankton, algae, and rooted plants. Tiny floating plants called phytoplankton are eaten by tiny floating animals called zooplankton. The algae that cover stones and rooted plants with scum or fur of green are eaten by such creatures as snails, tadpoles, minnows, and the larvae of many insects like mayflies and stoneflies.

Carnivores prey on all of them, and often on each other. Tadpoles become cannibals as they grow. Ferocious predators like the larvae of water beetles and dragonflies take anything they can catch and hold. Fish prey on the small carnivores, and are preyed upon them-

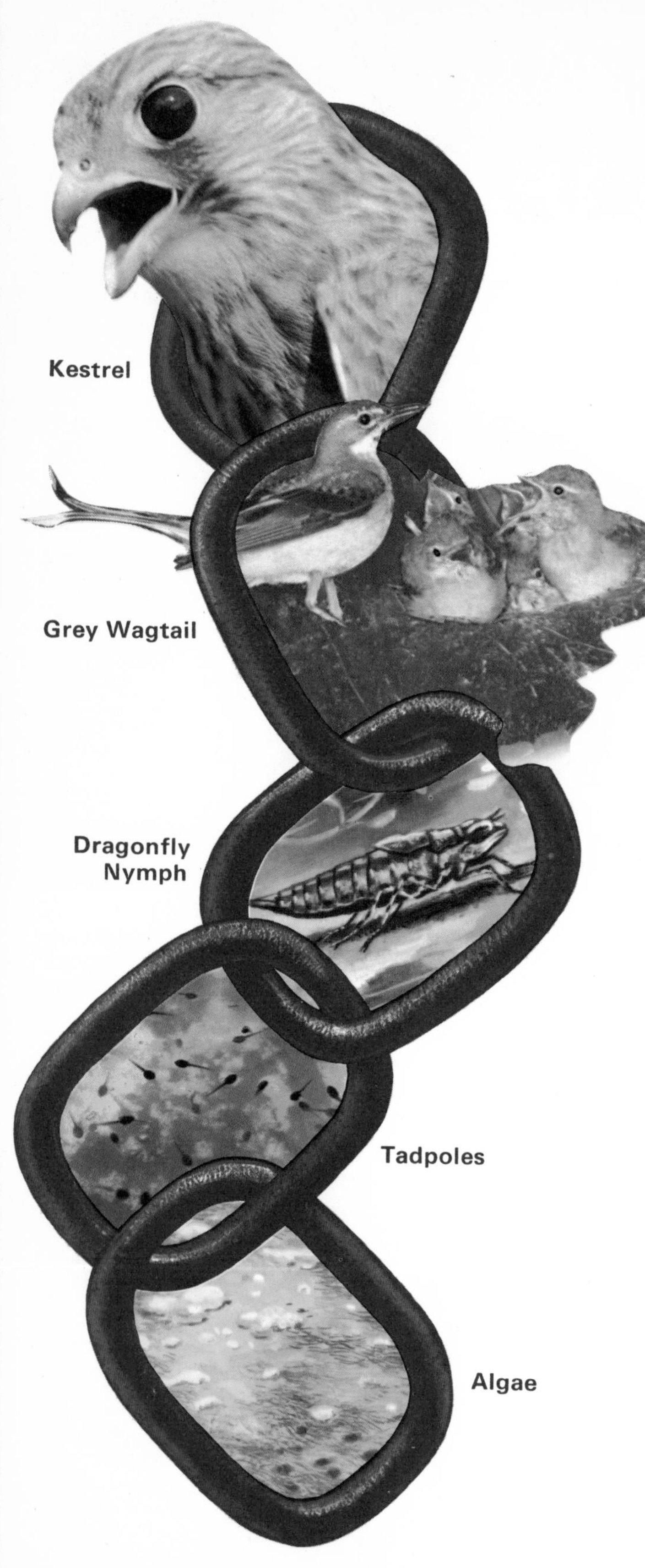

selves by bigger fish. Other predators—otters, mink, herons, and man—kill fish.

Water animals like dragonfly larvae become in time aerial predators that hawk flies, and are themselves killed by feathered predators like wagtails and swallows. Tadpoles leave the water when they become frogs, and are then eaten by land carnivores like herons, otters, foxes, hedgehogs, crows and buzzards. Water dwellers, like the whirligig beetles that live on the surface film, get some of their food from land when small creatures are blown in or fall in. Trout rise for such wreckage too, but don't seem to bother much with the whirligig beetles.

Any animal or plant that is not eaten falls to the bottom when it dies, where it is decomposed by the breakdown squads of bacteria and fungi, or eaten by scavengers. Many animals live on the bottom, feeding on broken-down matter; among them are some carnivores, feeding on their neighbours.

The pike is a fish at the end of many food chains, because it eats other fishes of many kinds, frogs, newts, water voles, water shrews, and the chicks of waterfowl, including ducklings.

Emigrants and engineers

The eel and the salmon are notable among fish, being commuters between fresh and salt water. Eels, born in the ocean, grow up in rivers, and are predators there, then return

A food chain is the order of eating in a habitat. Here the algae are eaten by tadpoles that are preyed upon by the nymph of the dragonfly which is eaten by a wagtail which is preyed upon by a falcon—the kestrel.

to the ocean to spawn. Salmon, born in rivers, are also predators while growing there; but they make their greatest growth in the ocean, to which they migrate as smolts, and when they return to freshwater to spawn they do not eat.

Beavers are the engineers of inland waters, and their activities can change landscapes. Their dams of logs, sticks, mud and stones give them the depth of water they need for their lodges, but also lead to flooding of the area, and the creation of marshes, which provide habitats for a host of new animals.

The beavers fell trees and eat the bark. Once they have cleared the trees from the edge of the marsh they move on, and the ground becomes lush meadow. With the beavers gone the dam begins to break up and is washed away by floods. The water level falls and the area returns to what it was before the beavers came. Later, trees begin to invade the meadow, making the site attractive again to beavers, and the cycle begins all over again.

Salmon leaping on their way upriver to the spawning grounds. European salmon may return to the parent river two or three times to spawn. Pacific salmon die after spawning once. All salmon grow up in the sea.

The Dragonfly is one of the hawks of the insect world.

Mallard drake on a frozen lake in midwinter. Mallards become quickly tame in association with man and will breed close to human habitations or even in gardens when not molested. They are important sporting wildfowl.

CHAPTER 8

PREDATORS AND PREY

A predator is an animal that kills other animals for food; the act itself is predation. The domestic cat, as everyone knows, is a predator on mice, and predation is a sort of universal cat-and-mouse act, performed endlessly on the ecological stage, in great variety of styles, by a cast of millions.

Obvious examples of predators are lions, pumas, wolves, eagles, goshawks, herons, crocodiles, sharks and pike. Lesser examples are the toad and frog. And all the insect-eating birds. And the tiniest shrews. And the wasp carrying home caterpillars for its larvae. And the larva of the water beetle sucking the insides out of tadpoles. And the tadpole itself, just as much as the whale which feeds on marine zooplankton—or man, the universal predator, who has the widest variety of skills and the greatest destructive power.

Prey range

There is an upper limit to the size of prey any predator can deal with, and a lower one below which the size of the prey is too small a return for the effort expended in catching it. Between these limits lies the predator's prey range. It goes outside its range only when there is extreme scarcity of prey within it. Thus European buzzards and golden eagles have been observed taking nestlings from the nests of small songbirds when their usual prey—hares, rabbits, grouse, voles—was scarce and hard to come by.

At other times a predator may concentrate on a single item within its prey range when that item becomes suddenly abundant and easy to catch—good examples of this being the white storks that follow the locust plagues in Africa; the jaegers that concentrate to prey on lemmings in Alaska; the short-eared owls that gather during a vole plague; and herons or otters that gorge on young frogs as they leave the ponds in late summer.

Does a predator that concentrates on an abundant prey species ever tire of eating the same food day after day? The answer from European tits would apparently be yes! These birds, which are similar to the chickadees of North America, were studied during the breeding season by Luke Tinbergen in Dutch pine forest where they were preying on a variety of caterpillars. When a caterpillar first appeared in the trees it was often rejected as food for several days, then suddenly the tits would begin to prey heavily on it.

Tinbergen thought that the tits acquired a specific *Search Image* of the new prey as they became more familiar with it. They formed a picture one might say. Once they had

The Red Fox is found in North America, Europe and in Russia.

Fledged Hen-harriers in defence posture. They defend themselves by lying over on their backs and striking with their claws.

their eye in, heavy predation followed. But it slackened off when the caterpillar became really abundant, as though the tits literally became "fed up" with it. No one caterpillar species ever made up more than half their food, which suggests that they preferred a mixed diet even when it was easier to fill up on one species. Thus there was a limit beyond which the tits were not prepared to prey on one species of caterpillar when there was a choice of other species available.

In this case the tits had such variety and abundance of food easily available that they could afford to be selective. Predation like this looks as easy as a fowl gobbling grain from a trough, and it very nearly is. The hard work for tits, warblers, and such birds, is fetching and carrying for their young. The parents have to visit the nest so often—at times every minute or so—that they could not rear big families in the short breeding season without abundant food, close at hand and easy to find.

But life is not always as easy as that, and the notion that a predator can go out and kill a prey the moment it decides to do so is not borne out by the facts. Sometimes it can; at other times it cannot.

Easy ways and other ways

In the first place, not all individuals of a predatory species are equal in prowess. A cock short-eared owl, for example, was seen killing only once in fifteen strikes, while his mate killed once in five. Some crows in nesting colonies are better at rearing families than others, partly because they are better providers, which means they are better hunters and foragers.

Youth or inexperience also accounts for many misses and near misses by the predator. But alertness of the prey also plays a part, because alertness among members of a prey species is no more equal than prowess is among predators.

There is no easy road even for the adult, experienced predator, which can also miss or lose a prey, especially if the prey is highly experienced. A fox can be left with a mouthful of feathers instead of the bird; or with a lively tail while the living lizard escapes. Lions often make a mess of a big prey animal without killing it. Many adult salmon, caught by fishermen, have tooth or claw marks to show that they have escaped from predatory seals.

What is it that makes a predator kill one thing rather than another at any given time? The short answer is: the facts of life. The prey species has to be there; it has to be available to the predator; it has to be within the predator's prey range; and it has to be palatable.

Given that the species is present, it has to be available, and its availability is determined by a number of factors: good or bad cover, age and experience of the prey, its speed and state of health, and its social standing within its group. Other factors play some part, their individual importance varying with the predator concerned. These are weather conditions—rain, frost, deep snow, strength and direction of wind; noises—groaning of trees, proximity of a river or waterfall; and competition with other predators.

Palatability of a prey species is not the decisive factor because it can only operate when the predator has a clear choice. A fox probably prefers pheasant to rat, but he is not likely to spend half the night chasing after an elusive pheasant and ignore the swarms of rats among his feet.

Sometimes a predator will kill what it does not like because, in the heat of the chase, it mistakes it for something it does like. This is probably true of the domestic cat, which kills shrews but does not eat them, yet goes on killing them presumably because it cannot tell the difference between a shrew and a mouse until it has made the kill. Shrews, on the other hand, after once killing an unpalatable species, recognize it later by smell and leave it alone.

Nobody knows how often predatory mammals make this kind of mistake, or how quickly they learn from it. Shrews are generally unpalatable to mammals because of their unpleasant odour, although some mammals will eat them when the alternatives are shrews or nothing. But one man's meat is another man's poison, as the saying has it, so we find that owls and hawks eat shrews readily and take them as they come.

The Common Partridge of Europe likes thick cover in which to nest, in hedge bottoms or in rough ground cover with scrub.

Any predator preying on any species meets the individuals of that species in a variety of situations. The quarry may be in thick concealing cover or in thin cover where it is more exposed. If more exposed it is more vulnerable and therefore more available. If it is mature and experienced it will stand a better chance of escape than the young or inexperienced, because it will know more about the tactics of the predator, more about the terrain, and more about escape routes.

The very young, and the very old crippled by injury, disease or hunger, are more likely to be preyed on than the healthy specimen in full prime. Social standing is a factor because an individual of low standing in its group will be a sort of second or third class citizen, forced on to the poorest ground, where the food is also poor, and where it will be more open to predation. The situation is also influenced by the age and experience—that is the prowess—of the predator.

These considerations affect all predator–prey relationships, but the importance of any one or several varies from situation to situation.

Selection of prey

The generalization that can be applied to all situations is that the predator takes what is most readily available. If two or more prey species are present, and one can be as easily caught as another, the predator will take them in proportion to their numbers. Where two are present, and one is a bit more difficult to catch than the other, this will be reflected in the rate of predation. The predator will prey more heavily on the easy one so long as it remains easy.

The marten in Scotland provides a good example of this. It preys on voles and woodmice, but kills more voles than woodmice, although woodmice are more numerous than voles on its territory. Traps on the same ground catch more woodmice than voles, so it is clear that the marten must find voles easier to catch than woodmice. This is probably because woodmice are alert and active, good jumpers and fast

The Common or Viviparous Lizard. When attacked or threatened by an enemy or even when roughly handled, the lizard may part company with part of its tail. This is known as self-fracture of the tail. As a result, a fox cub pouncing on a lizard may be left with a wriggling piece of tail while the lizard escapes with a bleeding stump. Later the lizard grows a new tail.

movers, whereas voles are slow scurriers.

The European mole provides another example of this kind of emphasis. It feeds mainly on earthworms, and when these are plentiful it disables and stores its surplus catch. Such stores have been investigated and have been found to contain mainly one species of worm, although several species were numerous on the pasture. Why the mole should do this has still to be discovered. But it seems clear that this worm is easier to catch than the others.

Predators also show selection within a prey species; they do not just chase the first individual they see.

The wolf of North America, which follows the migrating caribou herds, selects the calves, the aged, the sick and the wounded. The hunting dogs in Zambia prey upon hartebeest, but are selective. They kill more calves than yearlings; more yearlings than aged beasts; and more aged beasts than healthy adults. Lions on the other hand kill the age groups almost according to their proportion in the herd, which is a different kind of selection. Hyaenas, which are predators on the wildebeest of the Serengeti, kill only calves; yet another kind of selection.

Very often the prey selected by the predator is different in some way from other members of its group—making it, so to speak, an odd man out.

In Holland one third of the roach caught by cormorants are hosts to a tapeworm, although only one in sixteen of the roach population has tapeworm. This is a clear example of a predator selecting diseased prey in preference to healthy.

In Europe sparrowhawks and

North American Wolves hunting. The wolf pack is usually made up of dog, bitch and family, with perhaps one or two followers.

The African Lion hunts mainly the animals of the plains—antelopes and zebras. A male lion with his several mates make up the family unit known as a Pride. The male lion has a mane. Lionesses have no mane and are smaller and slimmer than males.

peregrine falcons have been observed selecting abnormal birds from flocks. Five birds out of twenty-three killed by sparrowhawks were found to be abnormal in some way, and one hawk was seen to take a lame blue tit from a flock of twenty healthy ones. In Germany, fifteen out of seventeen homing pigeons killed by peregrine falcons were found to have been off course or strangers to the neighbourhood. In Poland, a hawk was observed to take a white dove from a flock of dark ones, and a dark one from a flock of white ones.

Competition

Man, the onlooker, and himself a predator, tends to see the wild predator as his competitor when it is preying upon wild species he may want for himself. Most of the world-wide hostility towards predators is based on this assumption, which has been clearly shown to be false in some cases, and is probably so in many more.

As a general rule it is more likely that the numbers of the prey species determine the number of predators rather than the other way round. A loaf of bread can feed only so many mouths.

In a survey into the Decline of the Red Grouse in Scotland many facts about predation clearly emerged, the most important being that predation has hardly any effect on grouse numbers, and is closely linked with the social behaviour of the grouse.

The red grouse is a territorial bird which feeds on heather, and lives and breeds on heather moors. The males hold territories which they defend against other males by aggressive display. The most aggressive males hold the best territories, the next in line the next best, and so on until all available territories are occupied by a breeding pair. Birds unable to find a territory are surplus and are pushed out to marginal or poor ground: bare hillsides, grassy areas along the banks of streams, or areas of scant heather affording little food or cover.

Predation on these outsiders is

Common Buzzards are scavengers as well as predators. They will feed on dead deer, sheep, rabbits or hares, especially in winter. In many places the winter population of buzzards is based on carrion rather than on living prey. The buzzard kills mainly small mammals.

The British Red Grouse is a valuable sporting bird. It lives on moorlands and hillsides where heather (the common ling), is plentiful. It requires good leafy heather to feed on and a good cover of heather to nest in. The most aggressive cock grouse hold the best territories. Man maintains the habitat by careful burning of the heather.

six times higher than on territorial birds. Many of them die of disease or starvation. Others emigrate to seek territories elsewhere. This ensures that there are not too many mouths to feed on the crop of heather; the ecologist would say that this territoriality acts as a buffer between the population and its food supply.

When grouse shooting begins in August the territorial system breaks down and the coveys are all at equal risk from wild predators and man. Human predation now takes a heavy toll of the grouse, although man does not always take the full annual production of birds, which means he does not kill as many as he could. As a result, there are surplus birds to be evicted when the grouse re-establish territories in the autumn.

Once again predation is higher on the outsiders than on birds holding territories. Once again many die, and many emigrate. And some are at hand to occupy territories that fall vacant for one reason or another. Thus the red grouse regulates its own numbers, and manage-

The Tawny Owl hunts from dusk to dawn, preying mainly on small rodents—voles, mice and young rats. It also kills a certain number of small birds. The owl does not build a nest. Instead it uses a hollow tree, or the old nest of some other species such as the crow, magpie or sparrow-hawk.

ment of a moor means managing heather rather than killing predators.

Interest and capital

Much predation is known to be like this—the predator living off the prey without reducing or controlling its numbers—living off the interest rather than the capital one could say. The mole, which feeds almost entirely on earthworms, makes no noticeable inroad on the overall number of worms in an area. The same was true of the stoat in Europe when the rabbit was common. In Palestine, where half the barn owl's food is the Levant vole, the bird does not even begin to skim the interest of the 25,000 voles on its range. Similarly, all the cats in the world make no difference to the world population of mice.

Nevertheless, there are occasions when a small predator might make its weight felt. The weasel, because it is small and can enter small burrows, might cause great havoc among a local population of mice or voles. In fact, confirmation of this comes from America, where McCabe and Blanchard reported spectacular destruction in a local population of deer mice by a series of weasel raids.

Insectivorous birds may at times play a part in preventing plagues of insects. In the case of the European tits described by Tinbergen, predation was heaviest on caterpillars when they were at moderate densities—the time it hurt them most. But once an insect plague is under way, predation by insectivorous birds has no effect at all.

The fact that birds can act as a brake on insects at some stage is important to man. The Germans, recognizing the value of the tits in their forests, provide them with nesting boxes to keep them there and ensure their co-operation. This is a biological control—birds instead of insecticides.

What about big predators and big game? Do they control it? The evidence available, though still scant, is persuasive, and there is no doubt that in some instances they do. The deer of the Kaibab are a famous example.

At the beginning of this century the Kaibab Plateau in Arizona carried a stock of 4,000 mule deer and a considerable predator force of wolves, pumas, coyotes, bobcats, and some bears. The deer, which shared the range with sheep and cattle, remained stabilized around 4,000 head. This was fewer than the range could have carried, and there is little doubt that the figure was held level by predators.

In 1906 the area was designated a Federal Game Reserve. The cattle and sheep were taken off to make room for more deer, and trappers moved in to kill the predators. In ten years 600 pumas were killed. In sixteen years 3,000 coyotes were killed. By 1926 the wolves had been totally exterminated. The deer began to increase, slowly, then quickly, reaching a total of 60,000 head by 1920, and 100,000 by 1924. This fantastic figure was far beyond the carrying capacity of the range, which was progressively damaged and beaten up. In the next two winters 60,000 deer died. By 1929 the herd was down to 30,000; by 1931 it was 20,000; and by 1939 it was down to 10,000.

In this case the predators controlled the deer and protected the range; their removal allowed the deer to increase and ruin it.

There was a similar balance, or equilibrium, between the topi antelopes and the lions of the Rwindi-Rutshuru plain in the former Belgian Congo. The antelopes increased greatly between 1918 and 1929, the period during which the lions were drastically reduced by intensive hunting.

The harmless European Grass Snake preys largely upon frogs. It is an excellent swimmer.

Case of two relatives

Competition between predators of different species occupying the same ground is more apparent than real, even if some of them happen to be hunting the same prey species some of the time or even most of the time. Changes in the habitat, or in the numbers or proportion of the prey species, can tilt the balance in favour of one predator or another, compelling a reshuffle of forces. Such changes no doubt affect one predator more than another.

In the weasel and the stoat, this

During the upriver migration of the Pacific salmon to their spawning grounds they are preyed upon by Alaskan Brown bears which assemble at special places to intercept them. The bears swim and wade in the pools and sweep the fish ashore with their paws, or snatch them in their jaws. At this time large numbers of bears can be seen along a short stretch of river.

relationship has been closely studied, and as these predators occur throughout the northern hemisphere they will serve as an example.

In Great Britain weasel and stoat are often found on the same ground, and where each can hunt the prey most suited to it there is no competition. The weasel is smaller than the stoat, a male weasel weighing about 150 grams against 350 grams for a male stoat. When the rabbit was plentiful the stoat preyed mainly on it, while the weasel was and is a hunter of voles. Under these conditions both predators did well. But following on the disease myxomatosis, which almost wiped out the rabbit in most parts of the country, the stoat became scarce while the weasel remained plentiful. The disappearance of an important prey species tilted the balance against the stoat, without affecting the weasel at all.

Young forest plantations in temperate countries provide ideal habitats for voles, which thrive in the luxuriant grass. In such a situation weasel and stoat feed almost exclusively on vole. Their relationship in this habitat has been intensively studied in Scotland. The weasel, because of its small size, can follow the voles underground. This the bigger stoat cannot do, so it has to live on those above ground, which are surplus. The weasel, by attacking the basic stock of voles, helps to reduce the surplus available to the stoat, but so long as the vole numbers are above a certain level, both predators can earn a living. There are, however, great fluctuations in vole numbers, and when the number falls below 45 to the acre the stoat has to move out. The weasel, on the other hand, can continue to catch enough when the voles fall below 18 to the acre. Voles have to increase again before the stoat can return.

An example of the pair in another situation comes from the Dutch island of Terschelling where water voles were numerous and doing great damage to trees. Biological control of the water voles was attempted by the introduction of 102 weasels and 9 stoats in 1931. The weasels disappeared entirely within three years. Within five years the stoats had exterminated the water vole and reduced the rabbits to a very low level. Control measures had then to be taken against the stoat, which had increased at a great rate, and which had begun to prey on wild birds of many kinds, and on domestic poultry and ducks. After 1939 a natural balance became established and the stoat, though still common, ceased to be a problem. Here the stoat was suited while the weasel was not.

In the U.S.A. the place of these Europeans is taken by the least weasel and the short-tailed weasel; the first is similar to the European weasel, and the second is really the stoat. But in the U.S.A. the short-tailed weasel (stoat) varies greatly in size from one part of its range to another. The largest races occur from Eastern U.S.A. north westwards to Alaska, and this is the only area where the least weasel is found living side by side with it. In western North America, where the race of the short-tailed is no bigger than the least weasel, the least is absent altogether. So the small that can exist beside the big is not found beside the equally small. From this it seems clear that the short-tailed weasel at its smallest has some sort of edge over the least weasel which enables it to exist where the least weasel cannot.

Harriers are long-legged, long-tailed birds of prey that nest on the ground in rough vegetation or in plantations of young trees where the herbage cover is thick. The birds prey upon small mammals and small birds, occasionally on larger prey. During the breeding season, when the hen is brooding small chicks, the hunting male will pass prey to her in the air.

CHAPTER 9

UPS, DOWNS AND CYCLES

Plagues of voles and mice, like plagues of locusts, have been recorded since biblical times, and Aristotle has left an account of the rise and fall of a mouse population that might have been written yesterday instead of more than two thousand years ago.

What Aristotle described was a plague in the modern sense of the word. The mouse population erupted, damaged crops and its own habitat, then collapsed until there was hardly a mouse to be seen. The same sort of thing still happens from time to time at the present day, when conditions suddenly favour a breakaway by voles or mice, and we still call the result a plague.

But not all increases in mouse or vole populations lead to a plague; in fact they seldom do. No population of animals ever really stands still, and in some, like the voles, there is a regular pattern of increase and decrease, of ups and downs, that is known as a Population Cycle. One cycle follows another with the regularity of night following day; there is no time gap in the rhythm. But once in a while rodents break away at the peak of the cycle, increasing far beyond all normal limits, and this is when a normal cycle becomes a plague. While it lasts, serious damage is done to the habitat.

The Short-eared Owl is a specialist predator on short-tailed voles.

Such cycles are the order in voles: the European Short-Tailed Vole, the Red-Backed Vole of Scandinavia, the Meadow Vole of the United States, and the Lemmings of Europe and North America. In these species the cycle covers four years during which the number of animals increases from a low level to a peak, then falls away again to the former low level. This new low is the beginning of the next cycle.

Peak and crash—voles in Europe

The cycles of two rodent species have been closely studied—that of the Short-tailed Vole in Britain and of the Lemming in Alaska.

At the beginning of the vole's cycle its numbers are low, perhaps 10 or 20 to each acre of occupied ground. Numbers increase slowly to begin with, and after the first lap, say about a year, may reach no more than 30 to the acre. On the next lap a similar rate of increase is maintained, so that after two years the number of voles to the acre will be about 60 or 70. After that it rises steeply and in the third year it could reach 200 or 300 to the acre, or more. This level is held for the third year, and perhaps into the fourth, when the crash comes.

Once in a while the voles maintain their high rate of increase and go on to reach plague numbers—a density of anything from 500 to 600 up to 1,000 to the acre. In either case the crash comes suddenly, in the autumn, so that the population is low again in the spring at the beginning of the new cycle.

At the time of the crash, and afterwards, the habitat has a blistered appearance; it lies derelict, scarred and beaten-up, not unlike a battlefield after the armies have moved on. In this devastation the dead, undercut grass can be rolled back by the yard like a moth-eaten carpet; the bleached tussocks come away in the hand like a wig from a head. Young forest trees, their roots eaten, can be lifted from the ground like pea sticks. Vole burrows and creeps are everywhere; the grass is honeycombed with their entrances. But the voles themselves are few, a cadre force on which the next cycle will build to a new peak.

With the big battalions gone, the vegetation begins to recover from the punishment of too many mouths and too many feet. The grass grows green again and luxuriant, providing cover and food for the breeding voles. Now they have plenty of elbow room. Gone are the jostle and bustle, the hurry-scurry, the stresses and strains of the peak in its heyday. Yet the voles multiply slowly at first.

The Bank Vole resembles the short-tailed vole but has redder fur and a longer tail. The tail is dark above and pale below.

In the early days of scant cover they are wide open to predation by foxes, stoats, weasels, cats, owls and hawks, and this puts a brake on them. Even when the cover thickens, a highly efficient predator like the weasel, able to follow them down their burrows, can hold them back a little, delaying the breakaway by hard killing. But predation can be no more than a holding action of brief duration. The breakaway happens eventually and no amount of killing, by weasels or anything else, can prevent the build-up.

Stoat carrying a vole into its den in an old wall.

And again up

Heavy predation cannot, however, wholly explain the slow start. It may be that there is something wrong with the voles themselves at this time, a sort of hangover from the stresses and strains of life at the peak of the cycle. Various experiments have been carried out to test this theory, without definite results one way or the other. Still, it is tempting to think that voles might be worn down by the pace of life at the peak of a cycle, just as people can age or crack under the strain of prolonged anxiety or privation.

Whatever the cause of the slow start, breeding speeds up after the cycle is under way. The females that have survived the crash will produce two litters that season; then they die, because few voles live to see their second winter. Young females from the first litter may in turn have families of their own before breeding stops for the year. This is usually in the autumn although, in some years, some females will breed right through the winter.

In the second year breeding is continuous, which does not mean to say that all the voles are breeding at the same time. Mature females will produce two litters before they die in late summer or early autumn. Females from the first litter will breed twice that season, but it is unlikely that those from the second will do so more than once. This rate of production is possible because females can breed at the age of three weeks, and can become pregnant again while suckling. Predation takes its toll, but the increase in vole numbers goes on.

The third year sees the big battalions at strength, and there are about as many voles on the ground then as in the fourth year. Yet the crash does not take place in the third year; it comes in the fourth. The obvious question is: why do the voles not crash in the third year? Nobody really knows. But it seems almost certain that they do something to their habitat in the third year that is not felt until the fourth.

And again down

The crash is inevitable, whether it follows a normal peak or a plague, so naturally there has been a lot of speculation about the cause. There has also been a lot of research into it. But so far nobody has come up with an answer that will satisfy everybody.

Predators were once looked upon as the main cause, and they are clearly involved, because they can be seen to increase and decrease in the wake of the voles. But predation is only a detail of the main picture. If predators are powerless to prevent a build-up, it is hard to see how they can cut to pieces the bloated population of the peak. A predator eats what it can hold—no more: but in killing what it needs it will make a bigger inroad on voles when they are low than when they are high. It is the percentage that matters. Ten voles killed out of twenty is heavy predation; ten out of two hundred is a tickle without significance.

Epidemic disease was another suggestion—an outbreak of some killer that almost wiped out the population. But there has never been the slightest evidence of epidemic disease in a population crash.

The most persuasive explanation—the one that cries out for attention—is failure of food supply and destruction of cover: the voles eat their habitat down to the ground and at the same time leave themselves naked to predation. It is a fact that, at this time, voles will eat food they usually ignore: rush

The marking of birds by placing numbered and coded aluminium rings on their legs is one of the modern ways of finding out where they go, how far they travel, and how long they live. Here a young Hen Harrier is having a British Museum ring placed on its leg by David Stephen. Ringing on an international scale has provided much information on bird migration.

Dr. James Lockie anaesthetising a stoat caught in a box trap during a study of stoats in young forest. The captive is anaesthetised for easy handling. It is weighed and marked for future recognition then released. By trapping over an area the zoologist can map out the territory of each stoat. The box traps do not injure the stoats in any way.

The Woodmouse, or Fieldmouse, is a nocturnal species. It will even shun bright moonlight. It feeds on nuts, wild fruits, seeds and bulbs.

stems, the bark and roots of trees. And they do become more vulnerable to predation. On the other hand, the crash has been observed in habitats where much apparently suitable grass food remained. But it does not follow that it met the needs of the voles. For instance it could have become of poor quality through loss of minerals by much grazing—as can happen to plants growing on tundra or peaty soils.

In any crash, surviving groups of voles are to be found living on patches of ground with good grass and cover: islets of prosperity in a sea of desolation. They are the lucky ones, whose plot of land has come through the long gnaw with something to spare, including the lives of its occupants; whereas most of the habitat has been stripped of everything, including the voles it can no longer support.

The affluent society

A characteristic of vole peaks, or plagues, is the way the predators react. Most striking of all is the influx of short-eared owls in a plague area. Where a pair of these might be found on four hundred or five hundred acres when voles are low, there could be ten pairs at the peak of a cycle, and forty pairs or more during a plague. Some of these will be birds, born on the ground, which stayed there because voles were on the increase; the remainder, and perhaps most of them, will have arrived from outside. How they manage to arrive at the right time is still a mystery.

The more numerous the voles the bigger the families reared by the owls. When the voles crash the surplus owls depart, leaving behind the few that can still find a living.

Resident predators, like kestrels, harriers, buzzards and tawny owls, can rear full broods when voles are high, where before they had losses due to hunger. Birds of prey on the fringe of the vole grounds now hunt there too, because the area has become no-man's-land or anybody's. Old frontiers break down. So it is not unusual, during peak or plague, to see hawks and owls sitting around so stuffed with voles that the tails hang out of their beaks. Eagles take a lot of voles at such times, and the living can be seen mingling with the dead on a ledge beside the eyrie.

Ground predators like the fox find life a bit easier at the peak of a cycle, and kill voles in large numbers. At this time a fox may well get the pound of food a day he needs by eating nothing but voles. Ordinarily he might kill 2,000 voles a year in the same neighbourhood, which is high predation, but not as high as 16 a day. Short-eared owlets, crawling in the grass long before they can fly, are also easy prey and he takes these for a change. But the vole is his bread and butter while it is at peak.

The stoat and weasel live almost exclusively on voles at this time, and the weasel may react to the local plenty by producing an extra litter of young; the stoat, limited by its particular physiology, can breed only once whatever the food supply. When the crash comes these related predators are differently affected. The weasel can go into burrows that the stoat is too big to enter, so the stoat feels the pinch first during a crash. The stoat cannot exist when voles are below 45 to the acre; the weasel can carry on when they are down to 18 or fewer. So it can be a permanent resident where the stoat is only a part-time one.

Thus the predators sort themselves out, some leaving the ground, others regrouping on it. The habitat begins to recover, the voles multiply, and a new cycle begins.

The Weasel hunts mice and voles, and being of such small size is able to follow them into their burrows.

To stay or not to stay

The lemming is the vole of the Arctic tundra, and is found in a variety of species right round the roof of the world. Like other voles it has a basic four-year cycle with a peak and a crash. But many lemmings move out when the crash is due rather than stay at home to die on a devastated range. This is true of Scandinavia; in the years when their numbers hit a high peak the lemmings emigrate in force. In Alaska, on the other hand, the brown lemming dies where it stands because it has nowhere else to go. Not unnaturally, the emigrants have caught the imagination, and they

are now part of folklore, like the American pioneers. They have been groomed for stardom in a wildlife drama that takes as much licence with the facts of life as Shakespeare took with the facts of history.

Lemming emigration is an exodus from a devastated range in search of new pastures, not a race to the sea in search of some long-lost immemorial route to Atlantis. Most of what has been written about the animals on the move is true. They do pass through towns and villages, they do swarm in fields, and they do fall over cliffs. Many drown in streams and rivers, and some fall into the sea. But the movement is not a rush to suicide. The sea was never their chosen destination, nor death by drowning their aim.

Obviously, not all the lemmings move out. Many remain to die by predation. And there has to be a breeding stock left or there would be no new cycle. The spectacular emigration of the lemmings conceals the die-off, just as the spectacular die-off in field voles conceals whatever emigration there is.

The brown lemming lives on the boggy coastal barrens of the Alaskan tundra, where the plant growing season is short—from seven to ten weeks. As the lemmings are active at all seasons, this growth has to keep them in food for a year.

Lemmings' cycle

Breeding begins when the snow melts in June. The young are born three weeks later, and are weaned at the age of a fortnight. Under the snow breeding goes on into the winter, although not all the females take part. Despite this, winter breeding can produce from two to four generations, and the population could increase a hundredfold, because the lemmings are sealed

An Arctic Skua on her nest at 60° North latitude. This species, like the Jaeger, or Pomarine Skua, is a predator on lemmings as well as voles and mice. It also robs the nests of other birds, taking eggs and young.

The Kestrel is a mousing falcon. Its style of hunting is to hover until it spots a prey on the ground.

away from their predators by the snow.

As the snow melts the predators gather in force—jaegers and snowy owls, and perhaps short-eared owls as well. The lemmings are now exposed, having lost their top blanket of snow, which has melted, and their undercover of vegetation, which they have eaten. So they suffer severe losses. Presently the lemmings become so thin on the ground that they are too much trouble to catch, and the new growth gives cover to the ones that have survived. So the predators go away.

At the peak of a cycle the lemmings can be as high as 15 to the acre; after the crash they may come down to one lemming to 10 acres. Of course this does not mean a solitary lemming in splendid isolation on each ten-acre patch. What it refers to is the density of the animals on the range as a whole. If the range was a thousand acres, and this was fenced round, there would be 100 lemmings inside the fence; but there would be a small group here, and another there, and another yonder, with uninhabited areas of many times ten acres in between. The surviving groups hold strong-points, you might say, from which the new generations spread out to fill the empty ground.

Predators kill about half the lemming population at the peak of a cycle, so they play a big part in the crash, which can leave fewer than ten lemmings alive out of every thousand there before.

The simple habitat

Lemming and vole cycles have one thing in common—both occur in simple habitats, which have very little variety of plant and animal species. Such cycles do not occur in more complex habitats with great variety of plant and animal species.

A simple habitat can be nature's creation or man's. One of nature's is the coastal tundra of Alaska, where the vegetation is made up mainly of four species of grass and sedge. This vegetation supports only two vegetarian mammals, or herbivores: the brown lemming, which is common, and the collared lemming which is not. These in turn support only three common predators—the snowy owl, the jaeger, and the short-eared owl. This is a small cast on a vast stage with few props.

In Britain, the cycles of the field vole occur in simple habitats created mainly by man: hill sheep grazings, rough pastures, and great plantings of young coniferous trees. In other more varied habitats, the voles behave differently and there is no cycle.

A habitat does not have to be barren, or run down, or poor, to be simple. The simplicity is in the lack of variety. Thus vast areas planted with one kind of tree, or under one kind of crop such as wheat or maize, or grazed by one type of animal such as the sheep, are simple in this sense. They lack variety. This means that any pest that finds such an area highly suited to its needs can overrun it in an incredibly short period of time. There is no barrier, put up by something it does not like, to stop its run of success. So plagues of mice and voles keep breaking out in parts of the world that are ecologically simple but economically rich—vast areas of field crops, or orchards, or forest, or grassland.

The Short-tailed Vole is found on rough pastures, hillsides and young plantations where it feeds mainly on grass. When its numbers become high it also damages trees. In simple habitats its numbers fluctuate on a four-year cycle. Its main predators are hawks, owls, stoats, weasels and foxes.

Plagues East and West

In the U.S.S.R. the vole that does most of the damage, especially in European Russia, is the European field vole already mentioned: the one known as *Microtus arvalis.*

Every other year swarms of voles and mice plague hundreds of thousands of acres, sometimes even millions of acres, in the U.S.S.R.—a scale almost beyond imagination. In 1932 twenty-five million acres were infested with rodents of this kind.

The Russians have noted a sharing out of the habitat where two or more species are found together. Where *arvalis* is found on the same ground as its relative *socialis*, the first occupies the damp areas and the second the drier ones, with *arvalis* shooting up in wet years and *socialis* in dry ones. Where there are several species present, each tends to separate into the bits of the habitat that best suit it, which means that they are not one problem but many, as each has to be dealt with according to its particular habits.

America is no more free from vole and mouse outbreaks than Europe or Russia. In 1926 California Voles and house mice invaded 11,000 acres of a dried-up lake that had been planted with maize and barley. By November the rodents had annihilated the crops, so they began to move out in search of food. Along seventeen miles of highway observers noted a dead mouse at every yard. At the height of the plague the mice and voles reached 80,000 to the acre, which works out at 17 to the square yard—a density undreamed of before or since.

Explosions

Outbreaks are not, of course, confined to animals with definite cycles. They are happening all the time with many insects, and they occur in species much bigger than either insects or voles, for a variety of reasons, but all under the heading of favouritism in the habitat. Something favourable has to happen to allow a species to erupt—improved food supply, or cover, or some upset that is to the advantage of the species, or a combination of these. In the case of the Kaibab deer of Arizona, which increased from 4,000 to 100,000 head in eighteen years, the prime factor was the removal of predators by man. Man killed the pumas, wolves, coyotes and bobcats, and upset the balance in favour of the deer.

A number of bird species that inhabit the forests of northern Europe irrupt periodically into Britain and other European countries outside their normal range. Crossbills, nutcrackers, and pine grosbeaks, which are eaters of cone seeds, build up their numbers on their home ground when cones are abundant. Then a lean spell comes along and they have to starve or get out. There is a mass movement away from scarcity, and irruptions into other countries. The waxwing, which is an eater of berries, does the same when the berry harvest fails or is poor in its northern home. Of these four, the crossbill and the waxwing irrupt regularly into Britain, the other two more commonly into other parts of Europe. Some crossbills stay to breed the following spring if conditions are favourable.

The migratory locust is another example. Its irruptions have been recorded for three thousand years. When it is not overcrowded it stays at home, but when the population erupts there is a mass exit, followed by irruptions into other places. Modern attempts at control of the locust plagues aim at finding them before they erupt from their home ground—their "stations of permanent survival", their starting places in short.

Pallas's sand grouse, an inhabi-

The powerful claws and talons of an owl. Owls have two toes pointing forward and two pointing backwards, unlike other birds of prey—hawks, falcons, eagles, buzzards and others—which have three toes pointing forward and the hind talon backwards. All owls have feathered legs and feet.

tant of the Asiatic Steppe, irrupts in years of food shortage, and nomadic tribesmen have a saying that "when sand grouse fly by wives will be cheap".

The red squirrel, which feeds on the seeds of spruce and pine trees, erupts in Finland in years when the cone harvest is heavy, with the result that there are too many mouths to be fed the following year if the harvest is poor.

But the surplus squirrels, instead of waiting on to die, move out to seek living room and a livelihood elsewhere. Thus they stock up other forest areas, where they will erupt in the first year of heavy cone harvest.

The record shows that a good crop of spruce cones follows on a warm, dry spell from June to August. A good crop of spruce cones is followed a year later by a good crop of pine cones. In a sixteen-year period there were seven heavy crops, seven moderate crops, and two poor crops. In the heavy years the squirrel numbers shot up; in the not so good the extras marched out. The Finns try to control the squirrels by mopping up the surplus before emigration begins, and kill about 1½ million animals a year. The same ups and downs in squirrel numbers occur throughout the northern forest belt, but control is not so strict as in Finland.

An example of eruptions that cannot be explained is provided by the Hudson Bay Fur Records: subject—the raccoon. The usual catch was around 4,000 animals a year, but in 1875 it was 8,000, in 1897 it was 8,000, and in 1899 it was 14,000. A year well below normal was 1867 when the catch was 2,400. On the assumption that the trappers were trying their best all the time these figures indicate rise and fall in the numbers of raccoons. But they cannot be explained.

CHAPTER 10

WILDLIFE POPULATIONS

An animal is an individual. It may live alone for much of its life, or with a few of its kind, or in great herds; but singly or together the individuals are members of a species. The population of a species in an area is the sum of its individuals, just as the population of New York or London or Paris is the total of individual citizens living there.

Animals can have a real social life only if they are able to communicate with each other. Woodlice under a stone, or water fleas under the light in an aquarium, are mere gatherings of individuals. Their interest is in their surroundings, not in each other. They are no more a social unit than people in a bus queue.

Social animals communicate with each other in all sorts of ways. Birds sing, lions roar, grasshoppers make music, and ruffed grouse drum. Deer, antelopes and weasels leave scent to advertise their presence. The scent may be from a special gland, or from urine, or faeces. Many birds, insects and mammals display bright colours or conspicuous white marks.

The signal has to mean the same thing at all times, and to all members of the population. It may be simple, meaning no more than: *Here I am!* Or it may be complicated. But simple or complicated it has to receive the response: *Message Received and Understood!*

European Roebuck with antlers well grown in the velvet.

All in order

Peck Order is a term often used to describe the order of precedence in a society, and had its origin in the hen run, where fowls assert their authority over their inferiors by pecking. The peck order means that any bird can peck the ones of lower rank, but none of higher rank. The order is established in the first place by fighting, or by threat display.

The peck order works in some way in any animal society, so that there are dominant members having access to food, water, shelter and a mate, before any of those below them. The others down the peck order get their turn when the ones above have been satisfied. The order may be fixed originally by fighting, but once established it is accepted by all, so that display is then enough to enable the dominants to assert their rights.

African baboons live in large groups of about 80 animals. These are made up of sub-groups, each with a master male and his harem, and some inferior bachelor males. When the baboons are on the march, the inferior males take the front and rear, which are the danger posts, while the masters with their females and young stay in the middle where it is safer.

Red deer stags defend their females against other stags during

The white patch on the rump of deer is a signalling device between members of the species and is prominently displayed when an animal is running away from an enemy.

Red Deer hind with her calf in autumn in the Highlands of Scotland. Outside the breeding season the deer herd by sex so there are hind herds and stag herds.

the rut, partly by roaring and partly by just being there. If they have big antlers and a heavy mane, these may be enough to scare off their rivals. But if a rival is persistent it may come to a fight, and then the antlers are actually used.

Territory and display

Many animals hold territories which they defend against others of their own kind. The territory gives the animal a secure place in which to rear its young, and will have a good food supply within it or nearby. The animal, because it knows the ground, will be better able to avoid its enemies. Some animals, like weasels and stoats, hold territories throughout the year; others hold them only in the breeding season. Paired robins share a territory in spring, but hold separate ones in winter. Australian magpies hold territory as a social group, and fight intruders as a team.

A bird's territory may be no farther than it can see around its nest, or merely the space around a hole in a tree. Whatever its extent it takes two to draw the frontiers. The animals dispute, and the line where they call it a draw becomes the boundary between their territories. Much of the disputing is done by threat display, which accounts for some of the bright plumage of birds.

Some species hold gatherings for display, like Palolo worms, or male fireflies, or blackcocks in the spring. Even fish display. Male minnows and sticklebacks develop red breasts; gobies change colour and butt each other. Many mammals use scent to advertise themselves—weasels, foxes, bears, cats, some deer and antelopes. The hartebeest leaves its droppings along the boundary of its territory. The wildcat, unlike the domestic cat, does not cover its droppings, so they probably serve as territory markers. Cats and bears stand tall and claw tree trunks and branches, perhaps as a sign to others of their kind.

Members of a species do not all hold territories of the same size or quality. One piece of ground is better than another. The animals on the best ground do best, and the poorest animals are on the poorest ground.

This is very like what is known about the British red grouse. Holders of territory suffer least from predation and disease and are the ones that breed successfully. It may also be true of the hartebeest of Zambia. A master male, with his females and calves, holds territory. The biggest groups hold the biggest territories. The poorest habitats are occupied by bachelor males, and these may suffer most heavily from predation.

Social structure

The structure of an animal population is the number and sex of the age groups that make it up. These tell a great deal about the state of the population and its future prospects.

A population in decline usually has too many old animals and too few young ones to replace them. An expanding population has large numbers of young breeding animals and young being born. An established population has all age groups from the very young to the old. A stable population is one in which the births balance the deaths.

Many carnivores claw their height on tree stumps and posts. This is a badger's clawing post.

Male Black Grouse, known as Blackcocks, assemble in spring on a special display ground where they posture, display and call. The female black grouse is known as the grey hen.

The Mute Swan, widely known as a semi-tame bird, also breeds in a truly wild state in Northern Europe. It will lay up to eight eggs. The male swan, or cob, defends the nest by aggressive display and will attack intruders.

The Curlew usually lays four eggs, and clutches of five are rare. It is in fact notable as a four-egg bird. In the breeding season the curlew is found on moorlands, hillsides and rough pastures, but in winter it moves to bays and estuaries.

Family size and food supply

Each species has its typical clutch or litter size. A guillemot lays one egg, a blackbird 4 or 5, and a partridge 15 or 16. It would be surprising to find a woodpigeon sitting on 5 eggs or an eagle laying twenty. It is the same with mammals. Most African antelope have only a single young, but some deer have twins, and the Chinese water deer has 4 young at

a time. Mice have 4 or 5 young to a litter, the polar bear one or two, and the stoat between 6 and 9. Families above average size usually produce fewer young in the end because some die in the competition for food.

But there is room for adjustment. In a vole plague, owls will double the size of their clutch, or even treble it, and still manage to rear the whole family. When voles become scarce the owls lay fewer eggs or may not breed at all. So owls have remarkable ability to vary their clutch size, from 0 to 14. Other species have the same ability in some degree. It helps to keep the number of young in some sort of balance with food supply.

Birds like eagles, hawks, crows, cormorants and humming birds, which have their young in the nest for a long time, sometimes find themselves short of food in a poor season. They have a way of adjusting to this. The hen begins to incubate with her first egg, so that her young are born at intervals of a day or two. This means they are all of different size. If there is too little food to go round the youngest goes without, and eventually dies. If food remains scarce the next youngest dies. But usually some survive. This would not happen if all the young were of the same age and size, because all would share and all would go short.

Old and young

The number of young produced by a population is also affected by the density of the population. In overcrowded populations, perhaps also short of food, many members fail to breed, and young animals are slower in maturing. The ones that breed often have fewer young. The elephants of Murchison Falls in Uganda are presently at a high density and their young are not maturing until the age of 11 or 18 years. The normal is 8 years.

In wild populations it is unusual for animals to live to a great age. The actual life span is shorter than the possible, except in species without enemies, like elephants and man. In populations of ducks, game birds and songbirds, about half the adults die each year and are replaced by young. In gulls one in three dies, and in penguins one in ten. The rate at which a species loses members by death is the Mortality Rate.

The Social Wasps build elaborate nests of paper which they make from chewed wood. The nest is begun in the spring by the queen after she emerges from hibernation, and is built from the roof downwards. A mousehole is a favourite site. When the first brood of workers is on the wing they take over the work of building and the queen devotes her time to laying eggs.

Chicks of the Hen Harrier showing variation in size—the result of asynchronous hatching. The chicks hatch at intervals and the gradation of size means that during a food shortage the large chicks are fed while the small go hungry.

All young animals are vulnerable at birth. Baby mice and nestling birds are helpless because they cannot run or fly away. Young birds in a nest call to their parents to be fed. Where a brood is large, and food short, the young call more frequently and so attract predators. Predators account for most of the losses among young birds in the nest. In nests where the young are graded by size the smallest die of hunger in bad years.

Many young birds depend on their parents for some time after leaving the nest: blackbirds and tits for a fortnight or so, tawny owlets for several months. Gannets and shearwaters abandon their young in the nest, where they fast for a spell before making their way to sea alone. Mice and weasels look after their young for a short time after they leave the nest. Grey seals abandon their pups at the age of three weeks. The red deer suckles her calf right through its first winter, and it stays with her until the summer or longer.

Outsiders and insiders

Animals are distributed over an area in the habitats that suit them, and dispersed within each habitat according to their needs and social behaviour.

The African fish eagle is found near shallow waters where fish are easy to catch. It also scavenges near villages. In some areas it is most common beside villages. Villages are usually near the best fishing. So the eagle has the best of both worlds: scavenging and fishing. But there are no eagles in some areas where one would expect to find them. The eagles need dead trees as lookout places and in such areas there is none. Social behaviour also plays its part in keeping too many eagles from crowding into a good area, just as in the case of the Australian magpies.

Herons in England are not evenly distributed along the rivers; the bird is a colonial breeder and the biggest colonies are in the flood plains of the River Thames. The colonies are smallest where rivers are faster flowing and smaller. The size of a colony is decided by the supply of fish in the area. Surplus herons either do not try to get into a colony already at full strength, or are kept out by the aggressive behaviour of the residents.

If we think of all these things operating at the same time, the result is a balance. A population increases if recruits are more numerous than casualties; it decreases if casualties exceed recruiting. Elephants are the slowest breeders on earth, yet if they were allowed to increase unchecked there would in time be room for nothing else. It does not happen with elephants, and it does not with anything else, although there are occasional plagues of something.

Numbers are therefore regulated so that animals do not destroy their resources of food, water, shelter and cover. But how do they do it? There are several theories.

One is that species are constantly pushing against the limit of their food supply, but are kept in check by the peck order and the sacrifice of a surplus—as in red grouse.

Another is that species get some sort of warning of danger, and slow down breeding before the danger point is reached. When food is far in excess of needs the species speeds up breeding—as in owls.

Another is that stress of overcrowding causes a decline—as in voles.

Another is that many factors operate — weather, food supply, cover, predation and disease—and that one or other may be the most important at any one time.

Whatever the explanation, ecologists have not yet reached a conclusion.

Rooks are sociable birds. They return each spring to their traditional rookeries where they nest in the tallest trees. Old nests are repaired and used again but many new ones are built. The birds are also gregarious outside the breeding season and roost in large flocks.

Black-headed Gull at nest. About one-third of the gull population dies each year and is replaced by births.

CHAPTER 11

NEW NICHES FOR OLD

Animals and plants have not always remained on their home ground, in the niche they were born to. Birds and insects can fly; the walkers can walk. Plant seeds can be blown by the wind. So there have been breakouts from time to time, and successful colonizations as well as failures. But the world's faunal regions, and ecosystems, have on the whole remained notably stable.

Migratory species, although they may cross oceans and continents, fit into this because their movements are part of a stable pattern. They are commuters, with niches in two places. The common swallow has a summer niche in Europe and a winter niche in Africa; its flyways are part of the pattern and can be mapped. This is true of migrants generally—the ducks that fly across North America, the terns that cross oceans, the geese and waders of the Arctic that winter in Western Europe.

Many movements are accidental and come to nothing. There are lots of unwilling travellers. Birds and insects can be blown far out of their way by storms, and may or may not survive. Ocean birds like petrels have to come ashore to breed; but when they are blown far inland by a winter storm they die. This happened to large numbers of petrels in Scotland in the nineteen-fifties. About the same time an American sparrowhawk turned up on the west coast of Scotland, completing its journey by weather-ship, on which it had crashed, exhausted and emaciated, at sea.

Man as travel agent

But the most dramatic transfers of plants and animals from one part of the world to another have had man as travel agent, by accident or design. The results have often been disastrous.

The danger arises from turning an animal or a plant loose in an ecosystem to which it is alien, and where it has no natural niche. If the species cannot find a niche of some sort, or compete with the natives, it will of course die out. But if it is adaptable and can find a niche, it will survive. If it can take over several niches and displace natives, it may become a major pest.

An introduced species can therefore be a threat to the existence of native species, or cause an upheaval that leads to a reorganization of the ecosystem. It may increase to plague numbers and remain a plague, like the rabbit in Australia; or it may settle down at a lower level and reach some sort of stable balance with its new environment.

There may be a change in the make-up of the introduced species itself—a genetic change. This hap-

The Common Starling at its nesting hole on a British farm.

pened to the Mouflon, a wild sheep, which produced an entirely new race in Slovakia. In Czechoslovakia the introduced goat has bred with the native Ibex, producing hybrids that are weaker than the parents.

Man has been most successful with his introductions of domestic livestock and food plants to other parts of the world. The potato of South America has become a European staple. The horse, introduced to America by the Spaniards, played a major role in opening up the continent. Cattle and sheep replaced the bison millions of the prairies and plains. They were successfully introduced to Australia and New Zealand. They were introduced to Africa, where they have proved to be less able than the native ungulates to stand up to native pests and diseases.

Australia and New Zealand have been among the greatest receivers of alien species, taken there mostly by settlers who wanted some familiar faces among the unfamiliar native wildlife, which was like nothing they had ever seen before. Later introductions were of sporting animals or livestock.

The European Rabbit has proved one of the great colonisers. Australia's millions, like Europe's, were dramatically reduced by the virus disease known as Myxomatosis. The killing power of this disease seems to be weakening and more rabbits are surviving after each outbreak. The European rabbit is a major land problem in Australia.

Enter the rabbit

The introduction of the European rabbit was a major disaster for Australia. The first introduction was at Port Jackson in 1788. In 1859 Thomas Austin turned 24 rabbits loose in Victoria. Six years later he killed 20,000 and reckoned that 10,000 were left.

From then on the rabbit exploded in all directions, halted only by the desert and the tropics of the north. Thousands of miles of rabbit-proof fencing were erected without effect. Poison was tried but killed native species and domestic livestock. Then the virus of the disease known as myxomatosis was introduced. It killed off as many as ninety-nine out of every hundred rabbits. The survivors were immune to the disease, and they began to breed up again. The virus itself became weaker. So it looks as though the rabbits and the disease will strike a balance, with rabbits less numerous than before.

Rabbits in Australia cleared vast areas of scrub savanna by barking the trees, then prevented regeneration by eating down the seedlings. They over-grazed grasslands and let in weeds. They changed the whole environment to the detriment of the native species and introduced livestock. After myxomatosis farm production increased by £50 million in 1953. New Zealand, where the rabbit was also introduced, has tried to aid control by depriving it of commercial value—making it as worthless as rats or mice.

The new Australians

Australian native animals—marsupials and other types long isolated from the mainstream of evolution—have rarely been able to live on equal terms with modern introduced species. Long ago the Aborigines introduced the dingo, the so-called wild dog once thought to be a native. The wild dogs made their weight felt, and two native animals that suffered were the marsupial wolf, or thylacine, and the Tasmanian devil, a marsupial resembling the wolverine. Both are now thought to be extinct. Dingos nowadays interbreed with introduced domestic dogs.

The European fox, introduced to Australia for sport, preyed upon rabbits, which were a main prey at home. But it also preyed upon native species. Then it spread far beyond the limits of the rabbit, where it had to prey entirely on native species. It killed almost everything except the big kangaroos, and even these it chased until the young fell out of the pouch.

Stoat, weasel, and ferret, all predators on the rabbit in Europe, were brought to Australia to hunt it there but turned to native birds and small mammals instead. Just how widespread, or common, they are today nobody really knows. The European hare was introduced as a sporting animal some time after 1870, and is not a problem. It is found in Victoria, New South Wales and parts of Southern Queensland.

The Tasmanian Wolf, or Thylacine, is now thought to be extinct in Tasmania.

The Tasmanian Devil is a powerful animal, with strong jaws, persecuted in Tasmania because of its predation on small livestock.

The koala was in danger of being exterminated but is now protected by law. The koala gives birth to one young

The North American Grey Squirrel was introduced to England, where it was at first kept in confinement. Squirrels were later released because they were attractive animals. They began to spread and, as so often happens with an introduced species, eventually became a major pest. In Britain it is now an offence to keep grey squirrels alive in captivity without a special licence. Constant war is waged on the wild population. In many parts of the country, the grey squirrel has displaced the native Red.

island to a rocky, barren waste. Pigs now breed wild in many parts of Australia.

Rats and mice

All the species so far mentioned were introduced to other countries by deliberate human agency. But some introductions are accidental. The house mouse, once confined to Asia, is now the familiar prey of cats all over the world. The brown rat, a scavanger native to the Middle East, has colonized almost the whole world by man's agency. But nobody tried to spread the rat around. It travelled as a stowaway on ships. Britain got it via Norway which is why it is sometimes called the Norway rat.

The brown rat has been one of the world's great problems, partly because of its destruction of food at all stages of production, partly by fouling food, and partly as a carrier of various diseases, notably Bubonic Plague. Its saliva is dangerous. Its urine is dangerous. And its fleas are dangerous because they are the spreaders of plague. The black rat came to Western Europe earlier than the brown, and was also a disease carrier, but it has been largely replaced by its more forceful, colonizing relative.

Introduced diseases can be deadly to begin with because, being alien, they find a native population without any built-in resistance to them. It takes time for such resistance to build up. The disease has, of course, to find animals related to those it attacks in its place of origin.

Wherever there are cattle Foot and Mouth Disease can strike as soon as it arrives. The disease has twice been introduced to North America, but was wiped out by slaughtering the affected animals. It is established in Europe and Asia, but not in Britain where affected animals, and their contacts, are slaughtered when an outbreak occurs. Rinderpest was introduced to Africa by domestic cattle from Asia in 1890. It killed large numbers of big game animals, and many species still have not built up any resistance to it.

Two way traffic

Insect pests of one kind and another have been swopped around the world by accident in one way or another. The Colorado beetle of North America has invaded most of Europe, but is still absent from Britain and Scandinavia. North America has received legions of unwanted pests that have caused great damage to forests and orchards. Chestnut Blight, a fungus from the Orient, has cleared the eastern hardwood forests of the U.S.A. of chestnut trees. Dutch Elm Disease is now threatening the elms of the eastern hardwood forests. Pine weevils attack white pines; larch sawflies attack tamaracks; spruce bud worm attacks spruces in Canada; and bark beetle attacks the ponderosa pine.

An introduced pest can sometimes be controlled by introducing its natural enemy from the same source. The cottony cushion scale insect, introduced from Australia in 1868, threatened the citrus orchards of America. Control was achieved by introducing a predator from Australia—a beetle of the ladybird family.

At the end of the nineteenth century France was invaded by the American Vine Aphid, which lives on wild vines east of the Rockies. The wild vine of America is highly resistant to the root stage of the aphid. The aphid spread through the vineyards of Europe and North Africa, and its root galls killed the European vines. After 300,000 acres of French vineyards had been destroyed, an answer to the problem was found by grafting European vines on to American rootstocks.

From this it seems that it is as easy to get the wanted as well as the unwanted, but this is not always so. When an American cell biologist discovered a bacteria killer that was a great boon in cell research he was asked by cell biologists in other countries for cultures of it. But he had none to spare, and said so. Some of them started on the long, costly task of producing it for themselves. An English biologist had another idea. He took the letter he had received from the American biologist and grew the wanted bacteria killer from it. It had sneaked in with the mail, unseen, but there for the finding.

This is something like the man who had a jacket with buttons made from palm nuts. One day a grub popped out of a button when he was wearing the jacket. It had survived processing and manufacture to enter society via a button.

Ecological frontiers are the most difficult ones to guard against alien infiltration.

The European Starling, introduced to North America, has now become a problem species there. The original introduction was quite deliberate and was a great mistake as Americans now realize. Even on its home ground the bird has become a problem because of its habit of congregating in large numbers in cities during the winter months. It roosts on buildings, fouling them with its droppings. In the breeding season it poses no problem to the farmer. The problem in Britain is a social one of city hygiene.

CHAPTER 12

IN ALL ECOSYSTEMS IS MAN...

Ever since he gave up being a food gatherer and a hunter to become a food grower and a livestock rearer, man has made his weight felt in all ecosystems, using his great power for good or ill with almost equal freedom, and adjusting, improving or destroying habitats in a way no other species has ever been able to do.

His increase in numbers and the numbers of his settlements has been made at the expense of other habitats, which he has altered to suit himself. In the process he has displaced wildlife, and some species he has exterminated. By misuse of land he has created dust bowls and deserts, making the annexed habitats useless to himself. By wise use he has improved them. The tall green prairies of America have become the corn basket of a continent. Deserts have become productive by the wise use of water. Man, as trader, has depleted resources by export and import. But there have been advantages too. The farmlands of western Europe have been fertilized by the dung of cattle fed on grain and oil cake grown in the Americas.

Man's is the power, and sometimes the glory. He has created wildlife refuges, and set aside wilderness areas, to save species threatened by his expansion. The oryx, threatened in Arabia, has been given asylum in Arizona. Thoughtlessness destroyed the quagga and the springbok of Africa, the passenger pigeon of America, and the marsupial wolf of Australia. It almost destroyed the bison, once numbered in millions on the American Plains. The millions would have had to go anyway to make room for man and his livestock; but they could all have gone. Thought and effort saved some, and they are there for all to see.

The future of wildlife, especially big game animals and big carnivores, rests with man. He can destroy or leave alone; live with or without them. To have them means sharing living space with them, or giving them a place of their own. But this is only an aspect of conservation. Conservation also means wise use of wildlife resources, which means management, which is the business of ecology. Conservation by wise use is a basic concept, and applies to all natural resources, including land.

Man as destroyer

America suffered heavily from prodigal misuse of land and forests. Not surprisingly, immigrant farmers and stockmen, from countries with a long settled and highly productive agriculture, took their tried methods with them. They carried out vast operations, sometimes mortal, with-

Vast tracts of desert are being reclaimed to help support a growing population.

out suspecting their surgery. They ploughed where they should not, and felled where they should have left standing, and much damage was done before it was realized that the methods of France, England, Germany or the Netherlands, were not suited to many parts of America. Bared soil was blown away by the wind; cleared hillsides were eroded by water; deforested watersheds flooded the valleys.

Hundreds of thousands of acres of American farmlands, in Oklahoma, Nebraska, Dakota, Texas and Wyoming, were blown away by the wind before Hugh Bennett, a prophet in a dust storm, spelt out the answers, and in 1935 the 74th U.S. Congress passed the first soil conservation act in the history of the world.

Fire is still widely used by man as a tool in land use, mainly for burning off old growth to encourage young shoots to feed cattle, sheep, deer and grouse. Used with care it has advantages; carelessly used it can be disastrous.

Man-made fire is a world problem on tundra, savannas and mountain pastures. On the Taiga it can destroy the wintering ground of the caribou by burning the lichens. This is serious for the Eskimos, who depend on the caribou. In Africa, repeated burning of savanna degrades the soil and causes erosion. In the West Highlands of Scotland, where the hills are steep, the parent rock poor, and the rainfall high, burning is always dangerous, because erosion starts quickly and heather is replaced by fire-resistant sedges and grasses that are poor food for animals.

Careful burning can help birds like red grouse, which feed on heather. Burning makes for leafy growth, and if the moor is burned on a rotation basis, there will be heather of all ages from the newly sprouted to the deep and mature. This mixture suits the grouse; they eat it, breed in it, and hide in it. But as grouse hold territories of about 5 acres, the yearly fires must be small. If they are too big, large areas of ground are made sterile each year. The grouse suffer, and the bared ground is open to erosion, which prevents vegetation coming back.

Man the producer

By growing crops of one kind over wide areas man creates simple situations in which pests are likely to become a serious problem. His answer is to use powerful pesticides to kill the particular pest. But the pesticides can affect the whole ecosystem by attacking other species of animals and plants that are not pests. The destruction of the pest leaves a vacant niche which may be taken over by a worse pest. Or the original one may build up from immune strains to become a bigger pest than before.

Man reacts to failure by inventing new pesticides with still greater killing power, and with the same dangers for other forms of life. The hope for the future lies in more biological control, and the use of pesticides that hit a single target—the one they are aimed at. Pesticides pass along the food chain, and the persistent ones build up in the bodies of the final predators. The effect of such residues on predators is still being investigated.

Pesticides are used to help increase food production to feed an increasing world population. Part of our trouble is that we cannot eat grass or hay. We use animals to do it for us; then we eat the animals. If we could eat the grass it would shorten the food chain and put us

Modern man as a hunter—deerstalkers in the Scottish Highlands. Scotland has a population of about 200,000 Red Deer, almost all of them in the mountain areas. About one-sixth of the population is killed each year, hinds and stags being killed in the proper proportion. The weapon used is the rifle; there is no hunting with hounds.

Eskimos living in the Arctic have to be expert hunters to exist in such a harsh environment. With simple weapons like the hand harpoon and light canoes like the kayak, they hunt seals, walruses and other marine animals, which they use for food and clothing. The Eskimos also hunt the Polar Bear. Advancing civilization has brought them more amenities, often at the cost of their traditional prowess as hunters.

The Kalahari Bushmen are nomads, a primitive, pastoral people who have no settled territory. When hunting they use poisoned arrows, bows and arrows, knob-kerries and old cap guns. They eat small game, roots, birds, snakes, iguanas, fish, large mammals, locusts, ants, wild honey and even the lice on people. The bushmen are short, yellowish-brown men—the earliest inhabitants of South Africa of whom there is any reliable historical evidence.

Pup of the Atlantic or Grey Seal under three weeks old. The world population of grey seals is about 52,000 of which 35,000 breed on the British coasts. The grey seal is therefore a rare animal considered on a world scale and its conservation is a matter of concern. In Great Britain, the species is protected during its breeding season except for a cull of pups at one breeding station.

right at the energy source. Perhaps the possibility is not so remote. It has now been shown that high protein milk can be produced from a tall, tough grass. This grass covers vast areas of the Eastern Congo and is burned each year. Milk like that may not be very exciting, but it is a better way of using grass than setting it on fire.

Fish are an important human food, but here man often eats second and third line carnivores, well along the food chain, instead of the first line plant eaters. Fish that eat plants are produced in ponds in West Borneo. They even eat grass thrown into the water. We may yet get around to eating plankton and algae, the energy source again.

New sources of animal food may be discovered, like the termites used in the Congo. Termites are 36 per cent protein and 44 per cent fat, and provide 560 calories per 100 grams of termite.

Man has been extremely wasteful of many wildlife resources and nowhere more so than in his use of whales. Stocks have been so reduced by ruthless killing that nowadays only Russia, Japan and Norway bother seriously about whaling.

Fate of whales

Whaling dates back to the 10th century when Spanish and French Basques hunted with hand harpoons in open boats in the Bay of Biscay. Their hunting was a pinprick. The serious killing, a slaughter akin to that of the bison, began with the steam whaler, the harpoon gun, and later the factory ship. The Hump Whale was cut to pieces by

1913 when it became too scarce to be worth hunting. Then it was the Blue Whale's turn. It lasted until 1931, by which time it had become clear that far more whales were being killed than were being born. After the Blue, it was the Fin Whale's turn, and now it is on the way out. In 1948 the kill of Fin Whales was 21,000. In 1966 it was down to 3000. Only one Blue Whale was killed that year.

International agreements were made and in 1937 and 1938 total protection was given to Right and Grey Whales, and to immature animals of all species. Right and Grey Whales had become almost extinct as far back as 1904. After the war whaling began again, and for a few years the kill was within the limit set by the International Whaling Commission. In the 1950s more factory ships were built, and in the 1960s the agreed kill has been exceeded every year. Still the whale stocks decline, as ecologists have warned for years.

Once the numbers of a species fall below a certain level it seems to be unable to recover, and this is the danger to whales. The decline of whales is a sad testimony to the commercial greed of men, who are wiping out the largest animals in the world for present profit, instead of conserving them for future use. Whales, wisely used, could yield 350,000 tons of oil and 250,000 tons of other products every year into the indefinite future. They would also be saved as part of the world's wildlife heritage. How this can be done is known; how to get men to do it is the problem.

Conservation

Seals have also been ruthlessly hunted, often with great cruelty and the fur seals of the Pribilofs were almost exterminated before 1911, when an International Agreement laid down the numbers that could be killed on land and sea. Sealers from Russia, Japan, Canada and the U.S.A. had reduced the population from 1½ million to a few thousands. The population is now back at 1½ million, and the annual kill is over 50,000. This is conservation of a species while using it wisely: saving seals and a resource at the same time.

The saiga antelope of the European and Asiatic steppes also made a remarkable recovery from the edge of extinction. Its numbers had reached such a low level that the Soviet Union gave it protection in 1919, a remarkable act in itself because the country was torn by war. The decline continued until 1930, when only ten herds were thought to be left. Over-hunting, and competition with livestock, probably had something to do with this. Recovery began in 1930 and the population is now 2 million, of which 500,000 are taken annually by man.

In Scotland, which has 200,000 red deer, the annual kill is about 34,000, or 17 per cent of the herds. This is made up of selected males and females. Research has shown that a cull of 17 per cent crops the surplus without reducing the herds, which continue as a resource.

In parts of Rhodesia and South Africa game animals are now used as a resource instead of being cleared to make room for cattle. On thorn savanna they give a much higher return than cattle, sometimes as high as five to one, and more of them can use the ground because they graze in a spectrum. There are no overhead expenses with game, whereas cattle have to be watered and vaccinated against diseases to which the wild animals are immune or resistant. Present practice is to mix cattle with wild game or take the cattle off altogether.

The Red Lechwe, an antelope, has always been an important food animal for the natives of Zambia. A little over thirty years ago there were 250,000 lechwes on the Kafue Flats and 150,000 in the area of Lake Bangweulu. The populations were killed down to 50,000 and 16,000, mainly by mass hunting—the *Chilas* of local custom—and commercial poaching. The *Chilas* have now stopped, but it will be many years before the lechwe is back at its former level to provide a steady food supply for the human population.

Too much protection

Man sometimes steps in to save a threatened species by giving it protection. But he can overprotect. If he does this, for example by removing all predators, the habitat may suffer, and even the species itself. Absolute protection of the hippopotamus in Uganda has made it clear that there is no substitute for good management.

With human predation removed the hippos of the Kasinga Channel increased far beyond the carrying capacity of their habitat and spread out for three miles on either side. The result was overgrazing and erosion. But the increase of hippos had other unforeseen results. The increased dung in Kasinga Channel led to an increase in plankton and other water plants. This resulted in greatly increased fish stocks in the Kasinga and Lake Albert. So a canning factory was set up to make use of the fish. The offal from the fish attracted maribou storks. The storks roosted in a grove of rare Euphorbia trees and almost killed them with their droppings.

It was never the intention to kill off a rare tree, but overprotection of hippos almost brought this about. Now that the hippos are being controlled by shooting, it remains to be seen what will happen to the fish, the storks and the euphorbias.

Overprotection of elephants in Murchison Falls National Park, Uganda, also had unforeseen consequences. People were removed from the area because of sleeping sickness, and it was left to the elephants, which destroyed the tree cover and turned woodland savanna into grassland. This let in fires to destroy more trees, and the grasslands spread.

The elephants continued to increase, then after some years they began to suffer from overpopulation. Adult animals matured later than normal; fewer young were born; yearlings died from lack of shade on the open grassland. But

Hippopotamuses at the Kasinga Channel, Uganda. Protection of the hippopotamus here has shown that absolute protection is no substitute for good management. With complete protection the hippopotamuses multiplied to such an extent that they endangered their own environment and therefore their own existence.

these natural checks were not enough to reduce the large population to the proper level. Man has had to step in again and control by shooting. Native Africans were part of an ecosystem that needed them to help keep elephants in balance.

Man's grazing animals have affected ecosystems wherever he has moved. Sheep and goats made deserts in the Middle East; modern Israelis make farms and orchards out of them. The American pioneers made deserts out of rangeland; modern Americans are trying to unmake them. The Masai of East Africa count their wealth in cattle, and are unwilling to reduce their herds to numbers the range can support. The result is serious overgrazing. The Masai do not crop the wild game; they merely compete with them.

Wrong impressions

Man often looks upon wild grazing animals as the competitors of his domestic stock, but appearances can be misleading. Over much of Australia sheep share the grazing with kangaroos, which the stockman looks upon as competitors. In fact the kangaroos eat what the sheep do not want and do not take, which is the poorest grass. So there is no competition. The burning of scrub to create grassland for sheep also helps the kangaroos. The sheep change the vegetation by eating the best grass and leaving the poorest. The poorest becomes more common and this attracts still more kangaroos.

The red kangaroo has a similar association with cattle. In the dry season cattle eat long dry grass and drink at waterholes provided for them by man. The bitten grass sprouts green at the crown and this is eaten by the kangaroos, which get most of their water from this source and hardly ever drink at waterholes.

The Arabian Oryx, threatened with extinction in its native land, has been settled in Arizona where it is now breeding under control.

Soay Sheep on the Atlantic island of St. Kilda. This is a harsh environment where the death rate among the young in some years is very high.

Water is life

All animals need water in some form, including man who uses it for a great variety of purposes—drinking, irrigation, livestock, industry, hydroelectricity—and needs it in ever-increasing amounts. There is more than enough water in the world for human needs, but it is not always in the right place in the right quantity, and in some places the demand is greater than the supply. So the same water has often to be used again and again. Modern city dwellers regularly drink water that contains the indestructible residues of detergents. Londoners use water for drinking that has already been used several times.

Rivers and streams have always been handy places for dumping refuse and wastes. In modern times this has caused pollution of many rivers, with the death of fish stocks and other water life. Industrial wastes are poisonous unless cleaned before entering the water. Sewage in large quantities reduces the oxygen in the water, destroying life as a result. Modern sewage plants, which separate the solids from the water, help to correct this. The separated solids are then used to some extent as organic manure.

The needs of modern industry make water shortage a special problem in highly industrialized countries; yet in the midst of shortage flooding remains a threat to towns and cities on low ground. Men continue to live in areas liable to flooding because such sites have other advantages. Towns cannot be moved, but floods can be controlled.

In the United States of America, contour farming—ploughing along *the contours instead of* up and down *the hill—is one way of combating soil erosion. Although such erosion control methods are well understood, too frequently they are ignored. Both land and waterways are damaged as a result.*

Flood control begins at the watersheds, and watershed management is the beginning of water conservation.

Vegetation is the watershed's sponge and regulator of flow, and must be maintained, whether trees, shrubs or grass. In watershed areas the use of land for other purposes has to be carefully watched. For example, in the Scottish Highlands, the peat bogs above the tree line hold vast quantities of water, and that is their best function.

Dams can control floods and do other things besides, but do not always give complete protection. They are also expensive to build. Decisions to build dams cannot be taken lightly, because once a water system is tied up in this way, it is not easy to change it for other uses in the future. Short-term advantage can sometimes mean long-term loss to people and their way of life, as well as to wildlife, recreation, fisheries and the aesthetic values of the environment.

Water conservation by damming can be seen at its best in the Tennessee River Valley. The dams have converted the river into a chain of lakes, which give water for domestic use, electric power, irrigation, navigation and industry. They also give flood control. They also allow a breathing space for the restoration of eroded land, and the rebuilding of the shattered economy of the watersheds. The Tennessee Valley Authority is a model and an example to the rest of the world.

ACKNOWLEDGEMENTS

Cover picture by Douglas Botting. Endpaper pictures by David Stephen. Australian News and Information Bureau: pp. 38 (top), 42 (top), 111, 112. Des Bartlett: p. 14 (bottom). J. Morton Boyd: p. 124 (bottom). Jane Burton, Photo Researchers: p. 16. Charles Fracé: pp. 42 & 43 (bottom), 68 & 69 (bottom). Len Fullerton: pp. 49 (top), 51, 69 (centre), 72 (bottom), 73 (bottom left). Sven Gillsater: p. 84. Grant Heilman: p. 125. Patricia C. Henrichs: pp. 58 & 59, 70. E. Hosking, F.R.P.S: p. 31 (top). J. D. Lockie: p. 13. J. Martin: pp. 10, 11, 18, 20, 54 (top). Debs Metzong: p. 116. Grambs Miller: p. 53 (top). Robert Mitchell: p. 40. National Film Board of Canada: pp. 30, 31 (bottom), 54 (bottom), 55 (top), 58 (top), 63 (top right), 64, 79, 119 (bottom right). J. M. Nokes: p. 124 (top). Paul Popper Ltd.: pp. 34, 37, 38 (bottom), 39. Rhodesia Tourist Board: p. 63 (bottom right). Douglas Scott: p. 8. James Simon, Photo Researchers: p. 44. South African Tourist Corporation: pp. 23, 46, 47, 48, 49 (bottom), 50, 80, 119 (bottom left). C. A. Spinage: p. 123. David Stephen: pp. 6, 12, 14, 15, 21, 22, 24, 25, 26, 28, 29, 32, 33, 43 (top), 52, 55 (bottom), 56, 59 (top & centre), 60, 61, 62, 63 (top left), 66, 68 (top), 69 (top), 71, 72 (top three), 73 (bottom right), 74, 76, 77, 78, 81, 82, 83, 85, 86, 88, 89, 91, 92, 93, 94, 96, 97, 99, 100, 102, 103, 104, 105, 106, 107, 108, 110, 113, 114, 115, 119 (top right), 120. Ronald Thompson: p. 73 (top). Tierbilder Okapia: p. 65 (bottom). U.S. Travel Service: p. 45.

FURTHER READING

Andrewartha, H. G. and Birch, L. C. 1954. *The Distribution and Abundance of Animals.* University of Chicago Press.
Brink, W. 1951. *Big Hugh: The Father of Soil Conservation.* Macmillan.
Brown, L. 1965. *Africa: A Natural History.* Hamish Hamilton, London.
Browning, T. O. 1963. *Animal Populations.* Hutchinson, London.
Carson, R. 1963. *Silent Spring.* Hamish Hamilton, London.
Castro, J. de. 1952. *Geography of Hunger.* Victor Gollancz, London.
Cloudsley-Thompson, J. L. 1960. *Animal Behaviour.* Oliver and Boyd, Edinburgh.
Curry-Lindahl, K. 1965. *Europe: A Natural History.* Hamish Hamilton, London.
Darling, F. F. 1960. *Wildlife in an African Territory.* Oxford University Press.
Dasmann, R. F. 1959. *Environmental Conservation.* John Wiley and Sons, New York.
Dasmann, R. F. 1964. *Wildlife Biology.* John Wiley and Sons, New York.
Elton, C. 1927. *Animal Ecology.* Macmillan.
Elton, C. 1942. *Voles, Mice and Lemmings.* Oxford University Press.
Elton, C. 1958. *The Ecology of Invasions by Animals and Plants.* Methuen.
Graham, E. H. 1944. *Natural Principles of Land Use.* Oxford University Press.
Graham, E. H. 1947. *The Land and Wildlife.* Oxford University Press.
Grzimek, B. 1967. *Four-legged Australians.* Collins, London.
Hyams, E. 1952. *Soil and Civilisation.* Thames and Hudson, London.
Kendeigh, S. C. 1961. *Animal Ecology.* Prentice-Hall.
Lack, D. 1954. *The Natural Regulation of Animal Numbers.* Clarendon Press, Oxford.
Odum, E. P. *Ecology.* Holt, Rinehart and Winston.
Osborn, F. 1948. *Our Plundered Planet.* Little. Brown and Co. Boston.
Owen, D. F. 1966. *Animal Ecology in Tropical Africa.* Oliver and Boyd, Edinburgh.
Rudd, R. L. 1964. *Pesticides and the Living Landscape.* University of Wisconsin Press and Faber and Faber, London, 1965.
Serventy, D. L. 1961. *Fauna Conservation in Australia and Australian-controlled New Guinea.* 10th Pacific Science Congress.
Storer, J. H. 1963. *The Web of Life.* Vincent Stuart, London.
Tinbergen, N. 1953. *Social Behaviour in Animals.* Methuen, London, and John Wiley, New York.
Vogt, W. 1948. *The Road to Survival.* William Sloan, New York.
Worthington, E. B. and Macan, T. T. 1951. *Life in Lakes and Rivers.* Collins New Naturalist No. 15, London.

INDEX